CHAPELLE CREEK MEMORIES

Growing Up During
The Great Depression In South Dakota

❦

CHARLOTTE HYDE

literalpublishing

Edited by Charlotte's daughter, Terrill Hyde,
and her granddaughter, Tanya Huntington

D.R. © 2019, Literal Publishing
      5425 Renwick
      Houston, Texas, 77081
      www.literalmagazine.com

ISBN: 978-1-942307-31-0

Printed in the United States

In loving memory of my parents,
Charles and Polly Uecker

TABLE OF CONTENTS

My Mother,
the Eternal Optimist

To her the sky was always blue
(Even when it was a dismal gray).
The grass was green and growing
(When the dust was blowing it away).
The rain that fell was at least an inch
(Even though it barely wet the ground).
And when the wind and snowstorms raged outside,
She kept us safe and sound
By telling us stories of when she was a child,
How much fun she had every day
On the prairie north of Ree Heights
And somehow, our fears would go away.

When the food in the pantry was very scarce,
She'd find something, somehow, somewhere
And cook it up until it was delicious and hot;
Enough for us and some to spare

For anyone who happened by
(In the thirties, that happened a lot.)

She always told us tomorrow would be a good day
And our dad would find work on his very first try.
She would play her harmonica and we would sing
Songs like "Pretty Red Wing" and "Coming Through
         the Rye."
When our dad came home discouraged and worn
From a hard day of work without any pay,
She'd smile and say she knew tomorrow would be better,
And her confident air would chase our worries away.

As time went on, she added to her Best of Everything list:
Her children, sons and daughters-in-law are the very best,
Her grandchildren are her favorite friends,
And we must add the great-grandchildren to the rest.
For to us and everyone else she meets on her merry way,
We go away believing for awhile at least
That the sky is bluer, the grass is green
And the world's all right—
So says my mother, the eternal optimist.

THE HOME
ON NORTH CHAPELLE CREEK

Charlotte sat on the doorstep one spring day, kicking her heels. Daddy, Pauline, Clara and Marie had gone to the creek with their fishing poles, and she wanted to go along. She was nearly three years old, and she was almost as big as Marie, who was five. Clara was eight, and Pauline was ten. Her older sisters had promised Ma they would help Daddy watch Marie. Charlotte did not understand why they couldn't watch her as well.

Ma told Charlotte she was too little to go and had to stay home. She sat her on the doorstep and told her to stay there while she went into the house to get Charlotte's little brother, Ted. Ma said she would take them to the garden with her, and Charlotte could play in the dirt. Though it had always been fun before, Charlotte did not want to play in the dirt. She wanted to go fishing. She saw that the little gate at the end of the path was left open when Daddy and the older girls went through, so she decided she would go find them.

Charlotte ran fast, so Ma couldn't catch her heading down the trail towards the creek. She soon found herself surrounded by tall weeds. She decided she would go back to the house, but went the wrong way and stepped right off a steep bank that dropped down into the creek. She looked down and saw the water, so she grabbed a weed to pull herself back up. The weed came out by the roots and she grabbed another, which did the same thing. By that time, she was thoroughly frightened and started screaming and crying.

Just when Charlotte thought she couldn't hold on any longer, a big hand reached down, grasped her by the collar of her dress and pulled her up the bank. Daddy had heard Charlotte and come running to save her from falling into the creek. Pauline, Clara and Marie had followed and were watching the rescue, looking pale and scared.

Daddy didn't say a word. He carried Charlotte back to the house, put her inside and told her not to come out until Ma gave her permission. He went back down the path, closing the gate and tying it shut. Then he and the other girls picked up their fishing poles and returned to the creek.

Charlotte had learned her lesson. She didn't leave the yard for a long time, even when the gate was open, unless someone was with her. One day, after the older girls were in school, Ma sent Charlotte to tell Daddy to come in for dinner. On the farm, the noon meal was called dinner, and the evening meal was called supper. Sometimes, when Daddy and the hired man worked long, hard hours, they returned to the house in the mid-afternoon and had lunch as well.

Charlotte went fearfully through the gate and down the lane to the barn. Before she got there, she heard squealing and grunting and turned around to see a herd of pigs running towards her. Charlotte was scared. She screamed and ran back to the house. The pigs followed her. Daddy came out of the barn to see what all the commotion was about and found the pigs chasing her. He ran into the yard to drive them away, put Charlotte safely inside the house, then called the pigs back into the barnyard. And from that time on, even when she was in high school, Charlotte was scared of pigs.

THE HAPPY HOLLOW SCHOOL

When Charlotte nearly fell in the creek, the Uecker family lived on the Ditzler Place, located on North Chapelle Creek south of Harrold, South Dakota. Charlotte's older sisters, Pauline, Clara, and later on, Marie, attended school across the prairie at a small white building called Happy Hollow. When Pauline, who was the oldest, went by herself, she rode a sorrel horse called Dobbin. The next year, Charlotte wanted to go to school, too. Marie had taught her how to write her name and count, and she thought she was big enough. She would watch longingly as Pauline climbed on Pearl, their big saddle horse, and Daddy put Clara and Marie on behind. He would hand the girls their lunch pail and off they would go, trotting up the trail.

It was fun being the oldest at home, though. Charlotte and Ted would play outside in the tall grass near the house while Ma worked in the garden and took care of the chickens.

When September came the next year, Daddy put Charlotte on Pearl with the other three girls. Pauline sat in front and held the reins, then came Marie, who wrapped both arms around Pauline. Then Daddy put Charlotte on, and she wrapped both arms around Marie. The last one on was Clara, with her little legs sticking straight out as she sat back on Pearl's hips. Clara clutched a gallon syrup pail that held all their lunches in one hand while she wrapped the other arm around Charlotte. Pauline would kick Pearl in the sides to let her know everyone was ready, and they trotted off to school.

It wasn't far, but the girls had to cross a pasture where a big Jersey bull grazed with a herd of cattle, and Daddy and Ma were afraid he might chase them. There was also a pasture fence with a gate between the Uecker home and the schoolhouse, and Clara was in charge of the gate. She would hand the lunch pail to Marie while she slid off to open it. Pearl was a big, gentle, brown horse. She would go through the gate, then stop beside the fence. After she closed the gate, Clara would put one foot on the barbed wire and reach for Charlotte's hand. Charlotte clung desperately to Marie while she pulled on Clara's hand, and Pauline grabbed Clara's leg to help boost her back onto Pearl.

When they arrived at school, the teacher, Mr. Smith, would take the two littlest girls, Charlotte and Marie, off Pearl. Next, he would take the lunch pail, and then Pauline and Clara would slide off. Pauline would put Pearl in the barn, feed her some hay and run to the school-house before the bell rang.

There were several families who attended the little one-room country school. It sat alone on the prairie without any other buildings in sight. The school had a small entrance built onto it to serve as a cloakroom and hold the dinner pails. The other pupils were La Vera, Eugene and Robert Forthman; Glen Bronemann; Viola and Arlette Wasmund; and Katherine Nothdurft. Pauline was in the sixth grade, and Clara was in the fifth. Katherine and Marie were in the second grade, and Robert and Charlotte were in the first.

Mr. Smith was a stern teacher. He insisted that all the pupils' work be neatly done. If they didn't understand a lesson, he sent them to the blackboard and they went through it step by step until they understood. He was patient with the younger grades and Charlotte, Marie and Katherine owed their ability to read well and comprehend what they were reading to him. Charlotte only attended Happy Hollow School for a few months, but she was there long enough to get a good start in study habits that stayed with her all her life.

Mr. Smith lived on a farm near Okobojo, a small community near the Missouri River, north of Pierre.

He had a wife and several children who ran the farm while he was away. During the school year, he moved a small one-room shack to the school where he lived during the week. The shack was covered with tarpaper and had a little tin chimney sticking up from the flat roof. It was built on two long beams called skids, so he could pull it with his car or a team of horses if the roads were bad. The skids made it convenient for Mr. Smith to take the building back to his farm when school was out. He drove a Model T and traveled back and forth to his farm on weekends.

One day Charlotte, who was only five years old when she started going to school, felt very tired. It was a long time before school would be out, and she complained of a headache. Mr. Smith took her to his shack and told her to lie on the cot. There was only one room in the shack and it was bright and sunny, with white curtains blowing in the breeze that came in through the windows. A small combination cooking and heating stove stood on one side with a box full of firewood beside it. Sticky flypaper hung in a long curl from the ceiling, but there weren't many flies on it. A small table and two chairs occupied the center of the room. A red-and-white checked oilcloth covered the table with a tall jar of peppermint candy canes in the center. Mr. Smith gave Charlotte a small piece of peppermint, covered her with a bright quilt and told her to go to sleep, then went back to the schoolhouse to teach the other pupils. After the last recess was over, he came back and woke her up. She went back to the schoolroom feeling rested, and her headache was gone.

"Why did Mr. Smith take you to his shack? Were you naughty?" asked Marie.

"I don't know," replied Charlotte, who was only five years old. "I guess he could tell I needed a nap."

"What did you do when Mr. Smith left you and came back to the schoolhouse?" asked Pauline.

"I just lay on the bed and sucked on the peppermint stick he gave me, and I guess I went to sleep," Charlotte answered.

Several times after that, when he thought she was too tired, Mr. Smith would send Charlotte to the shack for a nap. Though the other children considered him a stern teacher, Charlotte thought him a kind man because he would sometimes give her a peppermint stick from the jar that stood on the table and would keep the older girls from scolding her when she was tired.

One afternoon, after Pauline helped Marie mount Pearl, she went to get Charlotte and Clara, who were still in the school's entryway putting on their jackets.

While Pauline was in the schoolroom, one of the older boys hit Pearl on the nose with a quirt. Pearl was startled and jumped to one side. Marie tumbled off, breaking her arm. Mr. Smith was very upset. He scolded the boy, and told Pauline to ride Pearl home. He put Clara, Marie and Charlotte into his Model T and drove them home. Ma and Daddy had taken the cream to Harrold and weren't there, so Mr. Smith stayed with the girls until they arrived. Then he and Daddy drove Marie to the hospital in Pierre, where Doctor Riggs set her arm.

Marie had to stay in the hospital several days. Her arm was broken at the elbow and when it was finally out of the sling, she had to carry a small pail of sand every day for a short time to help keep it straight. Although it seemed odd, this remedy was successful. Marie's arm healed without any of the stiffness or crookedness that at the time were usually the result of a break in a joint.

When snow came in the winter, the big boys from the school would put the small children, who had no overshoes, on sleds and pull them over the prairie. They would also include them in their games. Charlotte always liked it when Glen pitched in baseball, because he threw the ball at the bat and when she hit it, he would let her run to the bases without putting her out.

THE CHARIVARI

When the Uecker family lived on the Ditzler Place on North Chapelle Creek, two of the teachers who taught Hilltop School boarded there. Charlotte could barely remember the first teacher, Miss Jensen. She did not like small children, and she usually stayed in her room. The children had to be quiet when she went upstairs so their noise wouldn't bother her. Charlotte and Marie were told never to go near her room.

The next year, Norma Matteson was hired to teach at the little school that Clara and Pauline had started to attend. She loved children, and she and Ma became good friends. They would visit when she came home from school, and sometimes she would go outside with the children and play with them. She had a Model T car and she took Pauline and Clara to school with her. Her parents lived in Pierre, and she sometimes would take Pauline and Clara home with her on weekends so they could visit her younger sister, Rose. Everybody liked Norma, because she liked everybody.

Joe McKilligan started working for Daddy in the spring when he was planting crops. Though he usually went on to work at other farms after planting season, one year he decided to stay until the corn was picked. He met Norma when she began boarding with the family in September, and they started going to neighborhood dances and parties together. The children liked Joe too, because he would take time to romp and play with them when he came in for meals.

When hard times came and the Ueckers could no longer afford a hired man, Joe found work at another farm and Norma found a school to teach much closer to her home in Pierre.

One day, shortly after the family moved away from the Ditzler Place, Norma came to see them and told them she and Joe were getting married in the spring. They were going to live on a farm just a short distance away.

Ma and Daddy went to Harrold, and Ma bought them a nice sugar bowl and salt and pepper shakers for a wedding gift. Ma dressed up in a pretty green dress that her sister Elsie had sent her and went to the wedding in Pierre, while Daddy stayed home with the children.

When Norma and Joe came home from their honeymoon in Minnesota where his family lived, they came by team and wagon to visit. Ma told them that all of the neighbors were going to visit them that evening for a charivari (pronounced "shivaree") and bring cake and ice cream, so they would have to go home early.

"Oh, how nice!" exclaimed Norma. "Can we take Charlotte and Marie back with us?" Ma got them ready, and the two girls were lifted up on the spring seat between Norma and Joe. Joe shook the reins and said, "Giddap!" and the little black team, harnesses jingling, broke into a trot down the road to the McKilligan farm.

Charlotte and Marie were very shy. They had never gone anywhere without their parents and once they got out of Ma and Daddy's sight, they almost cried. Then Norma started talking to them and Joe sang a silly song, and they laughed the rest of the way to their farm. They tagged along with Joe to the barn while he milked the cows, then they all went to the house and ate supper.

It was nearly dark when Ma and Daddy and the other children arrived. They had waited for the rest of the neighbors and all came together. They banged on pans and tubs, rang bells and called out. Charlotte and Marie were frightened at first, but Norma told them it was all a joke, and they were welcoming them to the neighborhood.

Joe and Norma invited the neighbors into the house and passed out candy for treats. Then the ladies cut the cake and dished up the ice cream, and everybody visited while they ate. It was late by the time the party was over. Marie and Charlotte were both sound asleep when Daddy put them in the car to go home.

Charlotte attended many charivaris during her lifetime, including her own, but this was the first one and a special time for the Uecker family.

Joe and Norma remained good friends of the Ueckers. They later moved across the Missouri River to Mission Ridge where Joe worked at a ranch. They had three daughters. Norma and Ma wrote letters to each other, and Norma always sent pictures of their family.

The Home on the Side Hill

Charlotte was five years old when Dr. Martin and Mrs. Richards came one night in December 1927. The next morning, Daddy took the children into his and Ma's bedroom to meet their new baby sister.

Ma and Daddy always read stories to the children at bedtime. Ted's favorite was *The Three Bears*. He saw the baby snuggled up in Ma's arms and exclaimed, "Oh, there's Goldilocks!" Daddy thought that was a pretty name too, so they named the baby Goldie Mae.

After Goldie was born, Daddy and Ma lost all their savings when the Harrold Bank failed in 1929. They weren't able to continue to pay the cash rent for their farm to Mrs. Ditzler. Daddy wanted to rent the place on shares (that is, for a share of the crop instead of paying cash), but Mrs. Ditzler, who had also lost her savings when the bank closed, needed the money. She received a small down payment of rent from another neighbor, and the Uecker family had to move. She never received another payment and was sorry later on that she had made the decision to rent to someone else. In the end, she lost her farm.

Daddy had paid up rent for two years on a piece of hay land that adjoined the Ditzler Place, and he wanted to stay there until he got the hay mowed for the winter. So, he and Andy Jordan built a little house on a side hill. The hay land also provided pasture for Pearl, the brown saddle horse; Rosie and Blossom, the big white team; a bay mare they called Vixen and five milk cows. The rest of the livestock, except for some calves and chickens, was sold to pay for moving and the cash rent they owed Mrs. Ditzler. They built a lean-to for the remaining calves and chickens.

They also had a black dog with a white ring around his neck, a small white streak on his nose and four white paws. His name was Ring. He was a good farm dog and helped out by bringing in the cows at night.

There was no water at the little farm on the side hill. Every day or so, Daddy loaded barrels in the wagon and hitched up the team to go get water from the neighbors for the livestock and household. The house was not finished when they moved in and until they got some hinges, Daddy would have to lift the door away from the doorway whenever anyone wanted to go outside. He and Ma found some lightweight boards to make a partition for two small bedrooms. The house was crowded, but it was warm and cozy, and they lived in it for nearly a year. The Uecker family had a Model T Ford that Daddy had bought before the bank failed. Though he used the team most of the time, they drove the car when they took cream to town each week. The money from the sale of the cream went to buy groceries for the family. Daddy would take his team and wagon to work for the neighbors, but sometimes they wouldn't have enough money to pay him. This was the beginning of the "Hard Times" for people who lived on farms in the Midwest.

The new house on the side hill was very small. There was hardly enough room for the family of eight. Ma and Daddy and the baby slept in one bedroom. The other children slept in two big beds in the other bedroom. When the weather was bad, Charlotte and Ted would entertain themselves by jumping from one bed to the other. Charlotte would also watch the younger children when Daddy was at work, the older girls were in school, and Ma went outside to look after the cows and chickens.

When summer came and school was out, Ma hired a neighbor girl to stay with the children while she went out with Daddy to put up hay. Daddy wanted to get the hay mowed and stacked before harvest so he could hire

out with the team to help the neighbors with the thresh-
ing of their crops.

The house was away from the main traveled road, so
the family didn't get much company when the weather
was bad. Still, neighbors came to visit, and sometimes
Ma and Daddy would load up the family in the Model
T and go to the barn dances at the Henry Krull Place. Ma
and Daddy had held several dances when they lived in the
house on the Ditzler Place, and everybody in the neighborhood came, including Joe and Norma McKilligan.

Another neighbor, Claus Erp, who lived with his
family in a splendid big house on the hill, would walk
over the prairie to visit. He had a long white beard, and
Ted thought he was Santa Claus. Mr. Erp seldom rode
in a vehicle, though he was perhaps the most prosper-
ous farmer in the neighborhood. It was said that he had
walked across the state several times. When he went to
Minnesota and married Christina Jessen, he sent her
and her three children, Herman, Henry and Hannah,
to their new home by train while he walked back. Ma's
youngest brother, Ted Schenegge, would also ride his
horse from Big Bend to visit. He was in high school, but
would come to visit whenever he had a chance.

Ma and Daddy were popular in the neighborhood,
and Ma was an excellent cook. She always said the

neighbors knew when she baked bread, because they followed the smell to her house as soon as it was out of the oven. They never turned down anyone who needed help and sometimes, the family did without because of their generosity.

Though it was the start of the Great Depression, the home on the side hill was a pleasant time in Charlotte's life. She loved running through the tall prairie grass with Ring by her side, stopping often to listen to the meadowlarks singing and the wind blowing through the grass.

Gunny Sack Overshoes

Clara was crying when she came into the house on the side hill. The weather was cold, and Ma had kept Marie and Charlotte home from school. "My feet are cold," she sobbed. "I can't even feel my toes." Clara didn't have any overshoes. Pauline had a pair, but she was the only one who did. Two of the milk cows were dry, so there was very little cream to take to Bohning's Store in Harrold to sell in exchange for groceries and no money left over to buy overshoes for the younger girls.

One spring morning, Clara got up early and decided to start the fire in the heater because it was chilly. Ma had a small can of kerosene and she doused corncobs in it to start the fire in the morning. There weren't any corncobs in the wood box, so Clara tossed the kerosene into the stove by itself. It landed on some live coals and exploded, burning Clara's hand badly. Money was short, and Daddy could not afford gas for the car. He rode Pearl to a neighboring farm. The neighbor took him into town, where he went to Mr. Willard's drug store and got some salve to put on the burn. It took the pain out, but Clara wore a bandage on her hand for a long time.

The future did not look good for the family, but Ma, who was expecting another baby, said they had to keep their chins up. She said they were lucky Clara's hand was healing, and that they still had horses that could be hitched up to pull the wagon. The family still had livestock and some chickens, and everything would get better before long. Ma was always cheerful. She was a good cook, so the neighbors liked to come and visit, and she and Daddy made everybody welcome at their table.

The morning after Clara had cried because her feet were cold, Daddy came in from the shed with a pile of gunnysacks woven coarsely out of jute string and a ball of twine. The sacks would ordinarily hold about a bushel of potatoes, grain or coal. Twine string was used to tie bundles of grain before they were put into a stacked pile, called a "shock," to be threshed.

Daddy sat Clara, Marie and Charlotte down on the kitchen chairs and wrapped the gunnysacks around their feet. He wound the twine around the sacks and told the girls to walk around to see if he had tied them securely. The sacks around their feet and legs felt funny, but they would be warm. He lifted them up on Pearl behind Pauline, handed them the lunch pail, and they trotted off to school. When it was time to go home, Clara wound and tied her own gunnysacks, while Mr. Smith helped Charlotte and Marie.

"They're not so bad," said Clara, "once you get used to them. At least they are a lot warmer than no overshoes at all."

The girls wore their gunny sack overshoes when it was cold, and soon some of the other children also came to school with their feet all wrapped up in gunny sacks that were tied up with twine. Some of them left them on all day because they were difficult to tie, but Clara had learned to tie her own and later learned to tie Marie and Charlotte's, so they could take them off when they arrived at the schoolhouse.

The New Calf

"I know Mulie has a new calf, but I can't find it any-where," Ma complained as she came into the house and took Pauline's stocking cap off her head. Ma's sister, Aunt Elsie, had given each of the older girls a warm new cap and scarf for Christmas the year before. Pauline's was blue, Clara's green, Marie's pink, and Charlotte's brown. They took good care of them and Charlotte, who hadn't started to school when she was given hers, was still wear-ing it when she was in the eighth grade. The caps were too big for all the girls but Pauline, and Ma had stitched the sides up to make them temporarily smaller. Because Pauline's had not been made smaller, Ma borrowed it whenever she went outdoors.

"Maybe something got the calf," Pauline said fear-fully. She remembered hearing a coyote howl the night before. "No," said Ma. "Mulie has been nursed. She was sucked dry this morning, so I know the calf is all right."

Ma was exasperated. She had promised Daddy she would bring the new calf in as soon as it was born. Daddy was working with a road crew at the other end of the county. He and one of the neighbors stayed there in a small shack set on wagon wheels during the week, coming home only on weekends.

"We'll help look for the calf tonight, when we get home from school," promised Clara as she pulled on her cap. Ma took off Pauline's cap and handed it to her. Pauline pulled it down to her eyes then folded the bottom up, because it was too big for her, too. Then Ma helped Marie put her outdoor clothes on and went with the girls outside to help them onto Pearl and hand them their lunch pails. Pearl turned around and trotted down the road to take her charges to the little country school that stood a mile away from the house on the side hill.

Ma went back inside and looked through the window to see if Mulie had decided to go to her calf, but she and the other milk cows were grazing together at the end of the pasture. Ma had searched for the calf earlier that morning, riding Pearl into every ravine and looking into every tall clump of grass while Pauline and Clara watched the smaller children. Mulie was a clever cow, and Ma would have to watch closely if she was going to find it.

"I know that calf is in the pasture somewhere," she said to Charlotte. "I want you to keep looking out the window. If you see Mulie leaving the herd, call me. I have dishes and the cream separator to wash, and I'll never get them done at the rate I'm going."

Ma had to go outside to get water to heat so she could wash the breakfast dishes and the separator. Daddy had put two barrels in the wagon, hitched up the team, and gone to the neighbors' well to fill them before he went to work. She put wood in the stove to heat the water. She picked Goldie up from the blanket on the floor where Ted and Charlotte had been playing with her and nursed her while the water heated.

When Ma finished nursing Goldie, she poured hot water into the dishpan and washed the dishes while Charlotte, who was the big girl in the family when the others were in school, dried them. That didn't take long, but the cream separator took a lot longer, and Ma did that by herself.

Pauline and Clara had strained the morning's milk through a big clean cloth tied over the cream separator tank which had a faucet set in the bottom of it. The girls had to remember to turn the faucet off until they started separating because if they didn't, the milk would pour out on the floor.

When they were ready to begin, they reopened the faucet and started spinning a big wheel with the handle that was attached to it. The wheel turned a spindle on which the bowl that separated the milk from the cream was setting. When the wheel was turned, the bowl went round and round very fast. The milk went from the faucet into a round container with a float in it. From there it went into the cone-shaped heavy bowl, where the milk was separated from the cream.

The separator bowl had over twenty cone-shaped disks that had a number on each one. They had to be placed on the spindle that sat in the center of the separator bowl. The cones were assembled starting from number one and ascending to the final number. On top of them was a heavier cone-shaped disk that held the openings for the separated cream and milk to run into the spouts positioned over the bowl. The cream ran from one of the spouts into a container that sat on a small table that swung out from the separator stand. The milk ran from the other spout into a big bucket that sat on the floor. Each day when they finished, all of the separator parts had to be washed and scalded to keep the cream and milk sweet and pure.

While Ma washed the separator, Ted and Charlotte played with Goldie. And whenever Ma told Charlotte to check the window, she would climb on a chair and look out to where the cows were grazing. "She's still there," she would call to Ma. Then she'd climb down and play until Ma told her to look again. Every time she did, Mulie would be grazing with the herd, and Ma was puzzled indeed. "I can't understand why she doesn't go nurse the calf. It must be hid somewhere near where the cows are feeding. It could be that she's waiting until dark," she said, "and if that happens, the calf is going to be hard to find."

When the older girls got home from school, Pauline and Clara let Marie off at the door, then rode out to the pasture to look for the new calf. They searched until nearly dark, but they could not find it.

When evening fell and Mulie came in for water, Ma shut her in the corral. "I'll watch her closely after I let her out tomorrow," she said. "If she hasn't nursed it during the night, she will want to the first thing in the morning."

Ma watched Mulie closely the next morning, but she did not go near her calf. Ma was disgusted. She wanted the calf up close to the buildings, so it would be safe and she could feed it part of Mulie's milk. The family needed the rest of her milk, so they could separate the cream from it. The cream was taken to Harrold and sold at Bohning's Cream Station. They needed all the cream they could get because the money was used to buy groceries, but Ma couldn't risk milking Mulie and starving the calf.

Ma had just about given up when she saw Mulie go to the fence and look over the top wire. She stood there for a long time, and Ma was puzzled. "The calf must be on the other side of the fence," she decided. "I'll look there." She went to the barn, put the bridle on Pearl, jumped on her broad back and rode to the pasture heading straight to the fence. Mulie saw her and walked nonchalantly away to graze. Ma was starting back to the house to get the children ready for school when she spied something red under a huge thistle that lay in a small depression on the other side of the fence. "You old fox," Ma said to Mulie in admiration. "You really had me stumped." She had walked Pearl past that big thistle at least ten times thinking it was lying flat on the ground, not covering a baby calf in a depression under it. She jumped off Pearl and kicked the thistle aside to find the calf, a red-and-white heifer, lying very still. "You look just like your mother, but I hope you aren't as tricky as she is," smiled Ma as she pulled the calf under the wire, stood it up and started pushing it toward the barn.

When Mulie saw Ma pushing the calf, she ran towards her swinging her head and bawling. "Get out of here!" exclaimed Ma, waving Pearl's reins at her. Mulie had been a pail-fed calf and was a very gentle cow when she didn't have a calf to protect, so Ma didn't think Mulie would hurt her. Ma was wrong. Mulie nearly bunted her several times before she managed to push the calf into the barn and escape to the house.

Mulie was very angry. She kept bunting the barn door. Ma would go out to chase her away, and she'd come right back. Then Mulie, with a loud beller, charged the barn door and broke it down, and her calf came running out to stand by her side. Ma was determined she wouldn't hide the calf again. Pearl stood by the step, ready to take the children to school. Ma jumped on Pearl, kicking her in the sides to make her run, and caught up with Mulie and the calf. Ma dismounted and grabbed the calf by the head, then Pauline ran out to help her. "Let's put it in the house," Ma gasped, and the two of them dragged the calf to the door, pushed it into the house and slammed the door. Mulie stood for a moment, not realizing what was going on. But when the calf vanished from her sight, she ran toward the house, stopping short when the door slammed in her face.

Mulie ran around the house, mooing and pawing the ground. She then went and stood in a corner by the barn, shaking her head and mooing at the house.

Ma rushed the girls out to put them on Pearl, so they could go to school. "I don't think we should go," hesitated Pauline. "What if she tries to get into the house?"

"If she gets too wild, I'll shove the calf outside," said Ma. "Now, get off to school."

Ma pulled the calf into a corner by the stove and Ted, Goldie and Charlotte got as far away as they could, but only for a little while. They overcame their fear and crept closer and closer. Soon they were crawling all over the calf while it lay still and watched them. "Let me know when it tries to get up," said Ma. "I don't want it to get near Goldie. It might fall on her and hurt her."

The calf was too frightened to get up, but every once in a while would open its mouth and cry, "Maa-aa." When it did that, Mulie would come bawling from the barnyard and try to bunt the house. Then she would go back to the corner and shake her head.

Ma had wanted to wash clothes that day, but decided against going outside and making Mulie angry all over again. They all stayed inside until the girls arrived home from school. Mulie was tired by that time and Pauline, astride Pearl, managed to chase her out into the pasture.

When Daddy got home that night, he fixed the barn door, chased Mulie in, tied her to the manger, and milked her. They fed some of the milk to the calf, which Daddy had shut up in the calf pen. Mulie still pawed the ground and bawled, but she had calmed down enough for Daddy to take her to the tank to water her.

It rained over the weekend, and Daddy didn't have to go work on the road until it dried off. Ma was glad. She was tired out and needed a few days to get back to normal. Daddy and Pauline did the chores and carried in the wood and water. Clara stayed inside and helped her with the housework while the smaller children played outside.

Mulie settled down and by the time Daddy went back to work, she was gentle enough for Ma to milk. Clara and Pauline fed the calf part of Mulie's milk every morning and every night until it was big enough to drink milk from a pail. That milk had been run through the separator. It was called skim milk, and the calves that drank it were called "skim milk calves."

BLACKIE

"Blackie has nine little chickens, just hatched!" exclaimed Pauline as she burst through the door of the little house that stood on the side hill. The wind was blowing and a gust of cold spring air swept through the house.

"Close the door, Pauline," Ma ordered absentmindedly. She was sitting at the breakfast table, spooning oatmeal into Goldie's mouth while singing a song to entertain her and Ted, Charlotte and Marie, who were eating pancakes and syrup. Clara had been outside, where she and Pauline had been helping Daddy with the morning chores, but just then she pushed the door back open and came rushing in to help Pauline tell the news.

"What did you say?" asked Ma after Clara slammed the door shut. "Chickens," said Pauline. "Lots of them," gasped Clara, who was still short of breath. "Nine," Pauline said proudly. "I counted them."

"Oh, my!" exclaimed Ma. "We'll have to build a coop for them. I don't want Blackie roaming around the place. A skunk or chicken hawk might get them."

It was still early Spring, and the small hay-roofed shed Daddy had built was full of horses, milk cows, and the calves that had been weaned from the milk cows. The calves were fed milk from a pail along with a small amount of ground grain. There wasn't any room in the shed for Blackie and the chicks. They would be in danger of being stepped or laid on by the livestock.

When Goldie had eaten her oatmeal, Ma put her on the floor to play and reached for a pan. She got some potatoes from the big gunny sack that stood by the door and sat down to peel them. She had to fix an early dinner for Daddy, so he could go to the neighbor's farm where he had a job sowing grain. He had already put the end-gate seeder on the farm wagon, and was hitching up Rosie and Blossom. The seeder had a big funnel attached at the top to pour grain into the hopper. Down below was a row of metal slots. A chain ran some gears from the hopper to the slots, and grain would come out in a wide arc onto the ground that was to be sowed. Daddy would drive the team in a straight line down the field, and the grain would spread out from the hopper, sowing the field behind it.

When Daddy got to the end of the field, he would turn around and come back a certain distance from the track made by the wagon. The trips up and down the field were called "rounds." It took many rounds to sow the field, and Daddy would have to stop often to fill the hopper with the seed grain he had scooped into the wagon. The machine was dangerous, as Charlotte knew. Once when the seeder was on the ground, she had put her hand down in the hopper and Ted pulled the chain. It turned the gears, and Charlotte got a bad cut on her hand. She wore a bandage for a long time. She didn't want herself or Ted to be scolded, so she never told how she got it, and they both stayed away from the end-gate seeder after that.

The door opened again, and Daddy stepped through carrying a big basket of corncobs for Ma to burn in the cook stove. "I see the girls told you the news," he said, as he watched them put caps and jackets on the younger children, who could hardly wait to go out to see the baby chicks. "I'll try to get a coop built for them by the end of the week. I won't have time to do it before then. We will have to keep them in the house tonight," he added, picking up Goldie, who had started to cry when she saw the other children leaving the house without her. He sat down in the rocking chair and rocked her to sleep, while Ma finished peeling potatoes and put them on the stove to cook.

"I'll try to fix something," Ma replied, "but you'll have to find some boards somewhere. We still have to build a coop big enough for the fifty chicks we ordered from the hatchery for Pauline and Clara's 4-H project. I hope we can get it built Sunday, because the new chicks will be sent next week."

Charlotte, Ted and Goldie were pleased to have Blackie and her family brought into the house, and Ma had to watch them carefully so they wouldn't grasp the chicks in their hands. Their little hands could squeeze a baby chick too hard and it would die, and she knew only too well how sad they would feel if that should happen.

Ma found a wooden box, took some boards from one end of it and turned it upside down. She put some hay in it and set it outside the kitchen door. Blackie took her little chickens into the box and nestled over them, clucking and pushing them under her with her short black beak. Blackie was an old hen and the children's favorite, for she never flew at them or pecked them. She was a fighter whenever the dog Ring came near her, though, and he stayed warily at a distance while she pecked in the yard, finding seeds and small insects for her little brood.

Ring followed the small children whenever Ma put them outside to play, getting in front of them and turning them around whenever he thought they were getting too far from the house. Every night, he went out alone and brought the milk cows in from the pasture.

He was a good farm dog and had saved Ma, Daddy and the older girls many steps when they were doing chores. All the family loved him. However, Ring did not like to be tied up. He howled all night, even when Daddy went to the door and told him to be quiet.

One morning, after Ma had put Blackie and the chicks outside, she and Daddy heard a furious cackle coming from the yard. "That's old Blackie," Ma said.

"I don't think she is fussing at Ring," Daddy answered as he pulled his jacket on. "He wouldn't tease her."

Daddy rushed out of the house just in time to see something streak through the grass with Ring chasing after it, his chain pulled loose. Old Blackie stood by the box, still cackling, her feathers sticking straight out. Her neck was bleeding and her feathers were torn, but she was all right, just frightened and angry. Daddy knelt down to look inside the coop and was pleased to see the little chickens all huddled inside. Blackie was clucking away, still angry. She gathered her chicks under her and pecked at Daddy's hand when he tried to smooth her feathers. *Whatever it was didn't get them this time, but I'd better get a coop built tonight so I can fasten the door shut*, he thought. He knew the animal that had attacked Blackie wouldn't come back during the day, but he tied Ring near the box for protection just in case.

When Daddy got home that night, he and Ma built a small chicken coop with a tight door to keep Blackie and the chicks in during the night. "That should keep them safe," said Ma. "I don't know," replied Daddy. "I hope so." Daddy was certain the fast animal that had attacked Blackie was a weasel, and he knew it would keep trying to get at her. "I think we'll keep her in the coop in the daytime for a while," he said, "but Blackie and the little chicks are staying in the house tonight. You'll have to shut her and the chicks in the coop tomorrow and put feed and water inside for them. I have known weasels to come around in the daytime if they think they can find something to eat."

The next day, Ma took the box with Blackie and her chicks to the new coop. She set the box down inside and took them out. There was plenty of room in the coop, because she and Daddy had built it big enough for the new chicks that had been ordered from the hatchery. She scattered some ground grain mixed with oatmeal for them and put in a shallow dish of water. She went out, closed the door tight, and finished the chores while Pauline and Clara watched the small children before they went to school.

Pauline and Clara walked past the chicken coop the next morning when they went to help Daddy with the chores. "Oh, look!" exclaimed Clara. "Blackie and the

chicks are gone!" One of the boards was pried off the front
of the coop. Pauline was worried. She ran through the
farmyard, calling "Chick, Chick," but there was no black
hen or small chicks to be found.

"Don't worry," said Daddy while he harnessed and
hitched the team to the wagon. "Blackie is a smart old
hen. She'll be back by the time you get home from
school." He put the bridle on Pearl and led her to the
house. He lifted Pauline, Clara and Marie up onto her
broad back and handed them the syrup pail that held
their lunch. With the three little girls on her back, Pearl
trotted off across the prairie to school. Daddy went off to
work and Ma was left alone to do the housework, wash
the cream separator and wash clothes, and care for Charlotte, Ted and Goldie. Charlotte was nearly five years old.
She helped Ma by watching the younger children, but
she wasn't old enough to be left alone with them.

Ma was so busy, she didn't have time to go to the
chicken coop to see if Blackie had come back. When
the older girls got home from school, they rode up to the
step where Ma took Clara and Marie off the horse. She
told Pauline to water Pearl and put her in the barn and
feed her. "Put out some more feed for Blackie," she said,
"and be sure to put some water in her dish. I couldn't
get out there to do it today."

Pauline nudged Pearl in the side and she trotted off to the barnyard. A short time later, she burst into the house. "Blackie is still gone!" she cried. "I can't find her. I knew I should have looked this morning until I found her!" she wept. Pauline loved Blackie along with all the other animals, and she would hold her and pet her when she put feed out for her and the chicks.

"Don't worry," comforted Ma. "She'll come back. She probably ranged out farther than usual." Ma was worried, but she didn't let Pauline know it. She hoped Blackie had knocked the board off the coop door herself and was out in the grass with her chicks.

"Daddy will find Blackie for us," said Marie confidently, while she and Charlotte stood by the window waiting to hear the wagon that would announce Daddy's return. "I know he will," answered Charlotte. "He always knows where to look." Just then, they heard the wagon wheels creaking and turning and they rushed out the door to run to meet him when he came over the hill. Daddy stopped the team when he saw them and waited for Clara and Pauline, who came running from the barn. He jumped out to lift them all into the wagon. "Blackie's still gone!" they all cried. "What's that?" asked Daddy as he climbed back into the wagon to drive them to the barn. "Blackie's still gone," Pauline said breathlessly. "I've looked all over for her and can't find her anywhere."

"I'll look for her after I've taken care of the horses," said Daddy.

"We've put the feed out for them, Daddy," said Clara.

"Good girls!" exclaimed Daddy. "Now all we have to do is take the harnesses off and water them. I'll look for Blackie before I milk the cows, though."

Daddy looked and looked. He was late getting the cows milked. The children were in bed when he got back to the house from doing the night chores. The next morning, he looked again before he did the morning chores, but he couldn't find a sign of Blackie or the chicks. "I'm afraid the weasel got them all," he told Ma, who was stirring up pancakes for breakfast. The oatmeal and coffee were done, so Daddy poured himself a cup and dished up oatmeal for the children and himself. "I'll have to work on that coop tonight for the other chicks," he said, "so I'll come home early."

"You can leave for the field as soon as you are done eating," said Ma. "Pauline and I will milk the cows while Clara watches the little ones. I'll tell her to keep them away from the stove." Ma always worried about the small children getting too close to the stove when the older ones were watching them. "All right," answered Daddy. "That will make a day's work, if I get an early start." He hurried through his breakfast and was soon on his way to the field.

The next day Daddy, Ma, and the smaller children drove to Harrold in the Model T. They went to the depot and waited for the train to bring fifty little chickens that were peeping loudly in a cardboard box with a lid on it. The box and lid had holes cut in them and tiny wood shavings, called excelsior, were placed in the bottom to keep the chicks warm and dry. Daddy put the box in the back seat with Ted and Charlotte, who felt very important because they were told to see that the lid didn't come off the box and let the chicks out.

When the older girls got home from school, the chicks were already in the new coop peeping loudly, while Ma lit a kerosene lantern to hang from the top to keep them warm. She had planned on Blackie to help keep them warm too, as she never cared when other chicks crawled beneath her feathers. The other hens in the farmyard did not like strange chicks getting under their wings. "I'll keep the box they came in," said Ma. "If it gets too cold at night, I'll bring them to the house and put them near the stove."

Pauline and Clara were excited when they got home from school, because they would care for the little chickens for their 4-H project. 4-H was an organization for rural children to take part in that helped them learn skills in homemaking, poultry, livestock, gardening and farming. Under the supervision of the club leader and the United States Department of Agriculture, they learned how to sew, cook, can and preserve foods, care for poultry and animals, and become leaders in the community. The emblem is a four-leaf clover with an "H" on each leaf, which stands for Head, Heart, Hands and Health, and the motto is, "To make the best better."

The girls were to keep a record of how much feed they gave the chicks and how much it cost. They had instructions telling them how to care for the chicks, and they were supposed to write down in their 4-H manual everything they did to take care of them.

The chicks were three weeks old when Daddy found four dead ones lying in the coop. "Maybe they were sick," said Ma. "No," Daddy replied. He looked worried. "It was the weasel. I found where he got into the coop. He dug a hole in the corner and came up between the side and the floorboard. We are lucky he only got four. It would probably have been more if Ring hadn't chased him away."

The girls cried when they found the weasel had killed the baby chicks. Daddy comforted them, saying, "We'll just have to make the coop stronger. I could set a trap, but it is too dangerous to have one around with the little children and Ring playing in the yard."

That night, after supper, Daddy nailed tin over the boards on the outside, digging underneath and bending it to cover the floorboards. "That should keep him out," he said.

After the children had gone to bed, Ma made hot coffee and put it in a jar. Daddy loaded the rifle, took the coffee and went outside to sit near the chicken coop away from the direction the wind was blowing. Daddy had been a trapper in Canada before he married Ma, and he knew his chances of getting the weasel were slim, even if he did place himself where it would be hard for the weasel to catch his scent. The weasel did not appear, so the chickens were safe another night. Daddy was too tired the next night after working all day in the field, so he and the children piled rocks around the coop to prevent the weasel from digging underneath. He tied Ring to a stake right beside it, and the weasel stayed away.

The chicks grew, and feathers soon took the place of down in their wings and tails. Every day, Pauline and Clara measured their feed and wrote it on the 4-H chart and every night, they put the chickens in the coop and tied Ring beside it. Ring hated to be tied by the chicken coop. He would whine and howl. Ma and the children felt sorry for him, but Daddy said Ring was a watchdog as well as a pet, and it was his job to keep the chickens safe and sound.

Daddy always fed and watered the chickens in the early morning when he did the chores. After he hitched up the team to go to work, he let them out of the coop. As Pauline and Clara got ready for school, they would chase them closer to the buildings if they had strayed too far away.

One afternoon, Ring began yelping and growling, and Ma ran outside to see what was wrong. The weasel had gotten inside the pen, and all but twenty of the chicks were killed.

When Daddy got home that night, he found a sad family waiting for him. "I thought he had left," he said. "Let's get the chores done early and we'll go to the neighbors to see if they have a trap. I didn't get one before, because I was afraid one of the little ones or Ring would get caught in it and it would injure them. Now that you girls are out of school, you'll have to watch them all the time when they are outside."

After supper, Daddy, Ma and the children got in the car and they started down the road to the neighbors' farm. "I see something in the ditch!" Clara cried out. "Where?" asked Daddy as he stepped on the brakes. "Right there!" cried Pauline. "It's long and slim and it's going towards the barn!" Daddy jumped out and called Ring who came bounding up the road. He spied the weasel and chased after it, barking loudly. The weasel was quick, streaking through the grass in the ditch with Ring right behind him.

Daddy ran down the ditch and threw a tire iron at the weasel, injuring him. When the injured weasel saw he couldn't outrun Daddy and Ring, he ran up a fence post. He spat at Ring, who was yelping and biting at him. Then Daddy finished him off with the tire iron. "There," he said, throwing the dead weasel into the trunk. "It is still cool out, and I might get something for his hide. I'll skin him and take the hide to Harrold the next time we go. We may as well visit the neighbors, but we won't need to borrow a trap. It wouldn't be so bad if they would just kill what they need, but the weasel is a mean animal. He kills for the joy of killing. This is a big one. I wonder why he ran up that post when he could have found a hole to go down anywhere on the prairie."

"I don't know why, either," said Ma.

"I do," said Clara decidedly. "Ring drove him to it. He was getting plenty mad about us tying him to that chicken coop all day and night and he decided to catch it even if it was the last thing he did, and the weasel ran up the post to get out of his way. He didn't think Daddy would be there to help Ring out," she finished.

The children were sad about losing so many chicks, and it looked like Blackie and her chicks were gone forever too, but they perked up when Daddy announced that the neighborhood 4th of July picnic would be at the Ditzler Place among the big trees. Pauline, Clara and Marie were happy when they found they were to return to their former home. They were anxious to see the creek and have a chance to play with their classmates.

Ma got up at daylight on the day of the picnic. She made fresh yeast rolls and a big chocolate cake with white frosting. She also made a big potato salad with onions and radishes from the garden. She made Daddy's favorite homemade salad dressing from thick cream for the potato salad.

"I wish we still had Blackie and her chickens," Ma said. "They would be ready to fry by now, and I could fix a couple for the picnic."

"That potato salad looks like a good substitute," said Daddy, who had just come in with the milk and was pouring it in the cream separator tank. "You make the best bread in the neighborhood," he added, as he took a roll out of a covered dishpan and popped it in his mouth. "You won't have any trouble getting rid of these."

"That's enough," replied Ma. "Between you and the girls, we won't have any to take to the picnic." She shooed everybody away from the table while she spread frosting on the chocolate cake she had baked before she put the rolls in the oven.

Ma and the older girls gave baths and put clean clothes on the little ones, and when that was done, they and Daddy got ready. "I'm glad we don't have to do this every day," said Ma. "Much as I like to go to see the neighbors and have a good time, it's a lot of work to get everything and everybody ready and out into the car before noon." Everybody looked nice, and they drove merrily down the road to the picnic with Ma singing songs and the children joining in. Daddy just listened and smiled. He always said he couldn't carry a tune with a bushel basket, but he loved music and enjoyed listening to everyone else sing, especially Ma.

The Uecker family had a good time at the picnic. There were foot races, a ball throw and sack races for the little ones. After they had eaten, the men and the older children played ball and the women watched the smaller ones and visited. That night, they shot off fireworks in a field, and everyone exclaimed how beautiful they were.

It was late when the family arrived home from the picnic. Goldie, Ted and Charlotte fell asleep as soon as Daddy started up the car, and the older girls sat quietly in the back seat, tired from a long day at play. "We had a good time," Pauline said. "I got a little homesick when I saw the old place, but it isn't so bad here. You can see a long way, and it's cooler up on the side hill."

"It helped to go somewhere and not have to worry about that weasel," Clara said. "I wish we didn't have to have such bad luck."

"I agree," answered Daddy, "but we can always be thankful that we have good luck too. There are a lot of people in this world who have nothing to eat, and no place to live. We have it a lot better than that." By that time, they were home. The older girls and Daddy carried in the sleeping children and put them to bed while Ma gathered up the picnic dishes. They were all tired, but they hurried out to do the chores. "I see some tired faces," said Daddy. "As soon as we get done, we'll go to bed."

The next morning, Pauline went out to feed the remaining chickens. She stopped to pat Ring on the head. He was lying contentedly by the doorstep, glad his chore of guarding chickens was over. She skipped to the coop and stopped short. Something was making a clucking noise, and she could hear chirping. *Another hen must have hatched out some chickens*, she thought, but she hadn't noticed any hens setting on eggs. She peered around the back of the chicken coop. Old Blackie was there scratching for bugs, and all nine half-grown chicks were scratching beside her. The weasel was dead, and the danger was gone. Blackie had brought her family home.

The Scar

"Oh! It's a nice day today," Clara exclaimed when she looked out of the window. "Can we go sledding?"

"I don't know why not," Daddy answered. "There is a lot of snow on that little hill over there. I'll open the fence for you, and you can slide right over the bottom strand. The top one will be too high for you."

The girls had been anxious to go ever since they had gotten a new sled that they could guide for Christmas. It had "Arrow" painted in bright letters across the top. Daddy had put a rope through the holes in the steering bar, and it was ready to go. It had been snowing for the last two days. The hills were covered and glistened in the sun. They put on their coats, caps and scarves and opened the door, letting a blast of cold air inside. Ma pulled Ted out of the draft and pulled Charlotte back from the door so she could tie her scarf. "Don't let Charlotte or Marie go down by themselves," she cautioned. "They are too small to guide the sled."

"We won't," chorused the girls, and off they went to the side hill, Clara dragging Charlotte by the hand so she could keep up.

The girls spent the morning sliding down the hill, over the break in the fence that Daddy had fixed and far out in the prairie. Sometimes, they had to put Charlotte and Marie back on the sled and pull them as far as the hill before they had them get off and trudge back up.

"I want to go down by myself," Marie announced. "I guided it when I was in front of you the last time, and I can pull it back up."

"I don't know," said Clara. "Ma said..."

"I don't know why she can't," said Pauline. "She's seven now. Here, I'll put Charlotte behind her, and there will be enough weight for them to go straight ahead."

Pauline made sure Marie had her feet firmly on the guide bar, then put Charlotte on behind her. "Hold tight," she told Charlotte, and Charlotte gripped the sides of the sled. Pauline gave the sled a shove and they went flying down the hill. The sled hit a rut and veered and headed for the fence away from the break that Daddy had fixed, and Marie fell off.

Clara screamed and ran to catch the sled before it hit the fence, but it had picked up speed. She called to Charlotte to duck when it reached the fence, but Charlotte was scared and crying because Marie had fallen off. The sled hit the fence and a barb caught Charlotte in the forehead, cutting a big gash. She fell off the sled, and it careened on down the hill.

The girls were frightened. They forgot all about the sled and ran for the house, pulling Charlotte along. The blood was spurting from her forehead. Ma heard them crying and called Daddy from the barn, who picked Charlotte up and carried her into the house. Ma tightly bandaged the cut, and the bleeding finally stopped.

Daddy scolded Clara and Pauline. "I heard Ma tell you that Marie and Charlotte were not to go downhill alone."

"Marie wanted to guide it by herself," sobbed Pauline. "We thought there would be enough weight to take them straight down, but then they hit that rut."

"You'll listen to us after this," said Daddy. "We got the bleeding stopped, but it could have been a lot worse. There won't be any more sledding until I'm sure you can follow orders when we give them. Now I want you to do your chores."

Pauline and Clara knew that Daddy was angry, and they silently went off to do their chores. Ma wrapped a new bandage around Charlotte's head and sat her in a chair by the fire. Before long, Charlotte went to sleep, and Ma carried her to bed.

Charlotte wore a bandage around her forehead for a long time. The wound took a while to heal, and Charlotte had an angry red scar on her forehead for many years. It eventually turned white but could easily be seen the rest of her life. It would be Charlotte's sharpest memory of the short time the family lived on the side hill.

Moving from the Side Hill

The Uecker family lived in the house on the side hill when they had their first stroke of bad luck. Their beautiful white mare Blossom, who was part of a team with Rosie, had gone through a gate left open by a neighbor when he went into his cane field. She had eaten the new cane, which at a certain time of development is poisonous to animals, and died. The family was devastated because she was a pet, and because Daddy had earned much needed income by hiring out his team and wagon. Now he would have to pair Rosie with Vixen, a small bay mare who could not pull as much as Blossom did.

Not long after Blossom died, a weasel killed most of their chickens. Then Ring, their beloved collie, contracted distemper and died. Ring was both a family pet and a faithful farm dog. He could be sent out to the pasture alone to bring in the cows and calves. He used to watch over the children and would warn the family by barking if he thought there was any danger.

Times got harder. The side hill house was small, and Daddy had a chance to sell it to Asle Jordan. He left home one day to look for another farm. He had heard there was a small one in the vicinity of the Krull Place, where he and Ma had once lived and had many neighbors they liked. It too was on Chapelle Creek, but much closer to where the creek poured into the Missouri River at DeGrey. They sold the side hill house and made plans to move to their new home right after Christmas. The children would start school at Crocus Hill after January 1, 1930.

Pauline and Clara did not want to move. Pauline was in the sixth grade and Clara in the fifth grade. They had always attended Happy Hollow School and would be leaving their friends and classmates. Charlotte and Marie were only in the first and second grades, and though they liked Mr. Smith and their classmates, they were excited about moving to the new place.

One bright wintry day in January, some of the neighbors came with teams, wagons and hayracks. They loaded up all of Ma and Daddy's furniture and farm equipment. Daddy had hitched Rosie and Vixen and Pearl and a horse he was breaking for a neighbor to his wagon and hayrack. Ma's brother, Uncle Ted, came down with his saddle horse and he and Joe McKilligan drove the cows and calves. The family said "goodbye" to the little farm, got into the Model T Ford and started off towards their new home. When they were a little way down the road, Ma said, "Oh, I forgot the water pail, washbasin and soap." She had kept them to the last so they could wash their faces and hands and comb their hair before they left. Daddy ran back inside and retrieved the forgotten items, but he just picked up the soap and put it in the washbasin. The soap dish was silver colored and in the early morning light, Daddy did not see it.

When they got to the new farm, Ma saw that the soap dish wasn't there. She felt bad, because it had been given to her and Daddy for a wedding present by one of her sisters. Daddy meant to go back to get it when he helped Asle Jordan move the house to his place, but he forgot all about it when the time came.

The Ueckers' new home was a small farm that was called the Lamphere Place. The place was named for the family of that name who had homesteaded the land and built the house. Several families lived there after that, but it kept the Lamphere name. The house was on the bank of the creek, but there was a shortage of water when the creek wasn't running. It had a large kitchen and living room, and two bedrooms on the ground floor. There was an unfinished room upstairs. It had a floor made of wide boards, but the walls were not finished.

There was a window at each end of the room. The house was old and it was cold with the wind blowing around the windows, so the family lived in the downstairs portion. It took too much fuel to heat the upstairs, and there wasn't time to cut the extra wood, because Daddy had found a job helping build a new county road from Harrold to Big Bend on the Missouri River.

Daddy and a neighbor, Earl Russell, both worked on the road construction. Because the construction site was too far away to drive their teams to work each day, they lived during the week in a small shack built on wheels, called a sheep wagon. Their horses and those of the rest of the crew were used to pull the fresno scrapers and smaller scrapers to build the road. The fresno scrapers were pulled by multiple teams of horses to move large quantities of dirt, while the smaller scrapers could be pulled by one team.

Ma was grateful that the new baby waited until Daddy was home for the weekend to be born. Dr. Martin, who had cared for Ma when Charlotte, Ted and Goldie were born, still lived in Harrold, but he sent Ma to Onida to a maternity home to await the birth of the new baby. The neighbors took in the rest of the family while she was gone. Pauline and Charlotte stayed at George Mathews', who lived a short distance from the road to Crocus Hill School, the new school they started to attend when they moved to the Lamphere Place. Clara and Marie stayed at Folkert Krull's, and Mack and Goldie McMillan kept Ted and Goldie. Miss Krull, their teacher, boarded with her brother, Folkert. Each morning, she put Clara and Marie in her small car then drove a short distance down the road to where Pauline and Charlotte waited. They got in, and the little car rattled over the ruts the rest of the way to school.

Ma was gone for three weeks before she came home with the children's new baby brother, George, who was born on January 24, 1930.

When Daddy was away from home working on the road, Ma would have to go outside to do the chores and milk the cows. The older girls were too scared to stay alone in the house with the small children, so she would take all of them with her, except for George and Charlotte. She instructed Charlotte to sit in the rocking chair holding George and not to move. Charlotte was very frightened as she sat in the chair rocking her brother, as sometimes it was nearly dark before the rest of the family came back into the house. After milking the cows, Ma had to separate the milk from the cream. The cream was sold in Harrold to help pay for groceries, and the milk was fed to the children and used in cooking. What was left was fed to the calves.

George was only a few months old when the family moved to yet another new home further down Chapelle Creek, where they would live for the next nine years. Their new home was on land known as the Congdon Place. The house wasn't as big, but it was much easier to keep warm, and there was a nice big barn and sheds for the livestock. The farm also had a spring on a steep side hill and a good well with spring water.

The new home was only a half-mile south of the Crocus Hill School. The house was smaller, but the place was beautiful, nestled down in a valley with Chapelle Creek flowing on three sides. There were trees on the hillsides and on the creek. Big cottonwood, elm and box elder trees surrounded the house and barn, and there were cedar trees on the west side of the house. There was a barn with a hayloft and a shed attached, and a spring up on a tree-filled hillside. In the winter, the ice froze as the water ran down the hillside into the creek. This made for great sledding, along with the other hills in the area.

It was equally as pretty in the summer with the trees in full leaf, birds singing, and the creek running over the rocks to lull the family to sleep at night. In the spring, the smell of plum and chokecherry blossoms filled the air, to be replaced in June with the scent of the wild roses that bloomed all along the creek. It was a wonderful place for Charlotte and the other children to play, walking along the creek, inspecting birds' nests, trying to catch the fish that swam over the rocks and skipping stones across the water.

Though she appreciated its beauty, Ma did not share the children's affection for the place, because it was so isolated. The family's only close neighbor was John Gerlt, who was a bachelor. Not until his sister Minnie and her husband Bob McCue and daughter Kathryn moved in with him because of hard times during the Depression did Ma have anyone she could visit and "neighbor" with.

Many years later, when Clara, Pauline and Charlotte were in their seventies, they visited Roger and Delores (Jessen) Husted, who then lived on the Ditzler Place on Chapelle Creek. The house the Uecker family lived in had burned down, and a newer one had been built near to where the old one stood. Some of the big trees that surrounded the home had survived. Roger put some bales on a wagon, the sisters and other members of the family climbed in, and he took them along an old trail to where the house on the side hill had stood. There were a few remnants still there. They picked up an old license plate that had belonged on the Model T, some other objects, and a part of the soap dish they had left behind when they moved. The prairie grass waved in the breeze just as it did when they were little girls, and the sisters shared memories of when they lived there in the home on the creek.

CROCUS HILL SCHOOL

"Don't be so slow!" Pauline scolded, as Marie and Charlotte lagged behind her and Clara while they walked over the faint path that went up the hill from their new home on Chapelle Creek.

Pauline, Clara, Marie and Charlotte were excited to attend Crocus Hill School after moving to the Lamphere Place. Their new home was on the creek bottom. A hill rose above it to the northwest, and that was the direction of the school. The hill seemed very high to the two little girls, and they were tired after trudging to the top. They walked on a small distance, then had to go down a small knoll to a valley on the John Gerlt Place, then up another long hill. The schoolhouse was a short distance from the top. It was just a little over half a mile from their new home, but seemed much farther because of the hills.

Pauline was very impatient with her sisters and hurried them along. She was anxious to get there early and meet her new classmates. Pauline was wearing overshoes that had belonged to Ma, but Clara and the two smaller girls were wearing gunnysack overshoes, and they made it much harder to walk. Ma didn't want the children to wear the sacks on their feet as there wasn't much snow, but Daddy said that even though they didn't look good, the children wouldn't get chilblains or colds if their feet were warm. Pauline said she would carry the lunch pails home if Clara would wrap and tie the sacks around Charlotte and Marie's feet.

Charlotte was scared. She didn't want to go to school if Mr. Smith wasn't there to teach her, and she didn't know any of the other children.

"You know me," Marie said, taking her hand. "We'll stick together, because I'm scared, too." The two little girls walked down the narrow path through the valley and up the last hill.

When the children walked over that hill, they saw the schoolhouse for the first time. A gate was on the southeast side of the yard. It was a big gate made to let horses and wagons through, and it was closed. There was no small gate for the children who walked to school. They had to part the barbed wires surrounding the schoolhouse and crawl through, hoping the barbs wouldn't catch on their clothes and tear them.

Crocus Hill School stood on two acres of prairie above the John Gerlt Place. The previous owners of the place had donated the land, but John Gerlt now owned the pasture that surrounded the school. The school building was painted white. There were three tall windows on the east side and two on the north side. There was a big bell in a cupola built on the roof. A small roofed entry was on the south side. A red barn stood in the northwest corner of the schoolyard, and the children could see horses tied to the manger near the open door. A smaller building with a toilet on each side of it stood a short distance north of the schoolhouse. The west toilet had "Boys" painted on the door and the east toilet, "Girls." The small red building in between was the coal shed.

"At least we know which toilet we are to go to," muttered Clara, and Charlotte realized that Clara and Pauline were scared, too. Pauline's scolding was just to cover up the way she really felt.

Pauline and Clara climbed through the fence and held the wires apart for Charlotte and Marie. By that time, all of the other children were standing there to greet them as they started their new school.

Charlotte already knew Ivan and Ralph McMillan. They lived a short distance up the creek from the Ueckers and had helped them move into their new home. The McMillans had been Ma and Daddy's neighbors when they had lived near Miller before the children were born. They had since moved to Chapelle Creek and would once again be close neighbors to the Ueckers. The Uecker family had eaten several meals with the McMillans while they were moving.

The other children were Vivian, Annabelle, Evelyn and Elaine Hall. They rode horseback from their home several miles west of the school. Rose Cunningham and Bud, Agnes and Thelma Young lived just over the hill from each other. They were not far from the creek, each of their places nestled in a small valley southwest of the school.

"Hi!" called out a small white-haired girl. "You must be the Uecker kids. My name is Agnes, and I'm in the sixth grade. Come and meet the others."

Their new classmates were very friendly, and Charlotte wondered why she had been so scared. One of the Hall girls explained that the school had been named Crocus Hill by one of the former teachers because the crocus was the state flower, and crocuses grew all over the hills that surrounded Chapelle Creek.

A tall stern-looking woman with dark hair came out of the building and pulled on the rope that was attached to the bell in the cupola. The bell made a loud ringing sound that could be heard for several miles. It was nine o'clock, and time for school to begin. Pigeons flew out from the cupola when the bell rang, and Charlotte and Marie watched in amazement. The children all ran into the schoolhouse, and Clara took Marie and Charlotte's hands and followed Pauline into the building.

They went up the steps into the entry. It was called the cloakroom. There was a cupboard there to hold the lunch pails. On top of the cupboard was the water cooler, which was a huge crock with a lid on it. It had a spigot on the bottom. Each pupil had to bring a cup to hang on nails above the cooler. In the winter the water cooler was moved into the schoolroom so it wouldn't freeze.

A gray enameled washbasin sat next to the water cooler, and there was a glass soap container filled with liquid soap fastened to the wall above it. Next to the basin was a water pail that held a metal dipper with a long handle. Those who didn't have cups held the dipper below the cooler faucet to collect their drink of water. The dipper was also used to dip water from the pail to wash their hands. In the winter, water from another pail that sat on the stove in the schoolroom, was added to the water pail to warm it up for washing. The pupils had to wash their hands before they ate their lunch and when they came back from the outdoor toilet.

The door that went into the entry and the one into the schoolroom both had windows at the top that could be opened to let fresh air in while the doors were closed. They were called transoms.

The teacher's name was Miss Krull. She sent Bud and Ivan out to the barn to bring in some desks. They came back with only three. "That's all there is," said Bud. "The horses kicked the other two all to pieces." Miss Krull scolded them for not tying their horses up in the barn. She picked two of the desks for Clara and Pauline. "Marie, you and Charlotte will have to share the other one, and here is a reading book for you to share as well."

Marie was willing to share her desk with Charlotte if there was only one to be had. It was awfully big and their feet hung about six inches from the floor, but that wasn't what bothered her. What did was that she was to share a first-grade reading book with Charlotte, when she was used to reading from a second-grade book.

"B-but I'm in the second grade, and she is in the first. I need a second-grade book," Marie protested.

"Do not speak until you raise your hand, and then I may give you permission," admonished Miss Krull. "Now, I want everyone to get to work." She motioned Agnes to come to her desk. "You may go to the library and get the books for Pauline and Clara. They are in your grade, so you know which ones to bring. If there aren't any there, you will have to share yours with them. Now everyone get to work. We've wasted too much time already." From that day on, Charlotte and Marie were afraid of their new teacher.

The schoolroom had a high ceiling and wainscoting was nailed around the bottom third of the walls. It was painted gray. There were white curtains on the two long windows on the north side of the schoolroom and three long windows on the east side. The door to the hallway was on the south side. The floor was of medium-wide pine boards that were oiled. A big stove with a jacket around it stood in the northwest corner. The jacket had small squares with clover leafs embossed on it, and Charlotte thought it looked nice.

There was a small bookcase that held a set of *Book of Knowledge* encyclopedias in the corner behind the stove, and the tall north window beside it gave enough light to make it a nice reading corner, as Charlotte learned in later years. Over in the other corner by the other north window stood a tall gray bookcase. It held the teacher's books, paste, scissors and other supplies. A much larger bookcase called the Library stood in the southeast corner. It held textbooks, storybooks, and supplies used for drawing and Palmer Method penmanship classes. A globe hung from the southwest corner ceiling.

Blackboards were on the walls between the entrance door on the south side and on the whole west wall, except for the space behind the stove. A map case which held the world and state maps on rollers hung above the blackboard on the south side. Black placards with Palmer Method handwriting were hung above all the blackboards. There were large prints of paintings hanging on the other walls. There was a picture of a little girl and a big dog by Landseer, called *Saved*. The others were *The Gleaners* by Millet, *The Horse Fair* by Rosa Bonheur, *The Blue Boy* by Gainsborough, and one of a shepherd driving sheep called *Leaving the Hills* by Joseph Farquharson. There were large portraits of George Washington and Abraham Lincoln as well.

A flag hung above the Library, and the children stood, faced and saluted the flag every morning when the weather was bad. When spring came, they would stand in a circle around the big flagpole on the playground and recite the salute before they went into the school to start classes.

The teacher's desk was in the center of the room at the north end. There was a long bench with a back and a seat that folded up next to it. It was called the Recitation Bench, and the pupils filed in to sit on it when the teacher called their class. The first pupil in line pulled the seat down for the class to sit on. When the class was over, the last pupil to stand folded the seat back up. The pupils' desks were in rows in front of the teacher's desk. The schoolroom was a pleasant place, and Charlotte liked it very much. She would spend the rest of her grade school years in this room at Crocus Hill School.

When recess time came, the teacher called out, "In position." The children all sat straight in their desks with their hands clasped on the desktop. Then she called out "Turn," and they turned to the aisle on their right side. Then she said, "Pass," and they walked slowly out the door, through the cloakroom to the outside door, and onto the front step. As soon as they reached the step, they broke ranks and ran shouting into the schoolyard, where they would have fifteen minutes of exercise and play until the teacher rang the bell. They had one recess in the morning, an hour for lunch and exercise, and another fifteen minutes for recess in the afternoon.

School was out at four in the afternoon. The children with horses retrieved them from the barn and rode home. Rose's father, Bob Cunningham, came with his Model T Ford and took Rose and the Young children home. Pauline gathered the lunch buckets. Clara fastened the gunny sacks around her own and Charlotte and Marie's feet, and they slowly trudged home.

Charlotte and Marie were tired and hungry when they arrived home that night. Pauline and Clara were excited about their new school and classmates, but Ma sent them all straight to bed after they finished supper. "You are going to bed with the little ones tonight," she said. "You can tell me all about what you did in school tomorrow morning while you eat your breakfast."

FIRST AND SECOND GRADE
AT CROCUS HILL

Miss Krull, the teacher at Crocus Hill School, was strict. When she rang the bell, the pupils had to file in very quietly and go to their seats.

There weren't any small desks stored in the barn that would fit Charlotte and Marie, so Miss Krull sat them together at a desk where their feet dangled and the top came nearly to their chins. The school board had promised to bring them smaller desks from another school that had some extras, but they never got around to it.

Marie and Charlotte were both uncomfortable in the big desk. The slippery seat wasn't wide enough for two children to sit on. It was difficult to do their lessons and balance themselves on the seat at the same time. If Charlotte got too close to Marie, nearly causing her to slide off, Marie would pinch her to make her move back. Marie wasn't being mean, she just didn't want to fall off the other side and be scolded. Once Marie whispered, "Get over," and Miss Krull saw her. Miss Krull snapped at her to be quiet. Marie was timid, and she cried. Charlotte didn't like to be pinched, so she clung to her seat, grasping at the desktop to hold herself there. Most of the desks had storage under the desktop, but Charlotte and Marie's didn't. Their books had to be stored behind the seat, under a hinged cover attached to the desk. If they let the cover make a sound when they took their books and tablets out, Miss Krull would scowl at them and tell them to be quiet.

Sometimes the Uecker children arrived late for school. When Daddy was gone, Pauline and Clara had to help Ma with the morning chores. If baby George was cranky, Ma had to tend to him first. When he went to sleep, they went out to do the chores. Ma did not like to have Marie and Charlotte go to school without their older sisters. There were times when it was so dark, they could see neither the house nor the schoolhouse. They hadn't lived in their new home long enough to be familiar with the directions, and the path wasn't marked well enough for them to follow yet. She was afraid they'd get lost and wander into the creek.

The teacher had a rule that those who came in late had to stand in the front of the room with their arms in the air until she told them they could take their seats. Charlotte and Marie couldn't stand with their arms and hands above their heads very long before they would get tired and begin to cry. Then the teacher would scold them and tell them to put their hands up again, or they would have to stand there all day.

When Pauline and Clara told Daddy about the punishment, he did not like it at all. He had a day off from work and went to school with the children the next morning. He talked to the teacher, explaining why the children were late some mornings and asking that she punish the small children some other way. He suggested she put her arms above her head sometime and see how long she could hold them there without getting tired. Miss Krull must have tried it because after that, she had the children stay in during the first recess if they were tardy.

When Miss Krull called a class, that class had to march quietly to the Recitation Bench in front of her desk and read their lessons by turn. When they were through, they marched back to their desks. Miss Krull was strict, but she was also a good teacher. The little ones might have been afraid of her, but she helped them all with their work and made sure they handed it in to be corrected. If there was a mistake, she explained how to do it right. When they had a wrong answer to a question, they had to do it over until they got it right. She had fourteen pupils in all eight grades, and she worked hard with all of them.

Charlotte did not go to school for six weeks her first year at Crocus Hill. She was pale and listless and ran a fever nearly every day. Ma was worried and kept her in bed most of the time. When the weather got warmer, Daddy took her to the field where she rode between his knees on the plow pulled by the team of horses, so she could get some sunshine. Charlotte liked to sit in his lap and hold the reins, saying, "Giddap!" to Rosie and Vixen. Ma told Daddy that the sunshine and fresh air were helping her, and that she had started playing with the younger children again.

Even when Charlotte was well enough to go back to school, she would get very tired when she climbed the hills. Clara would take her hand and help her along. Charlotte still had headaches and was very pale, so she sat on the steps to watch the others play during recess.

One morning, when Ivan and Ralph McMillan rode past the Uecker girls as they walked to school, they saw Charlotte lagging behind while she climbed the steep hill that rose above the house. Ivan jumped off his horse and put her on its back, then jumped back on behind her. He rode a sorrel horse with a white blaze that ran from the top of his head to his nose, and Charlotte thought he was beautiful. Every day after that, Ivan rode to the Uecker home and Daddy would put Charlotte on behind him. She would hang on to Ivan tightly while the horse climbed the hill, then they would trot on to school, leaving the other children far behind. Ivan gave Charlotte a ride to and from school every day. He was a big boy for his age and didn't say much, but he was Charlotte's favorite new friend in Crocus Hill School.

Charlotte had a new teacher when she was in the second grade. Her name was Alma Lindberg. She was nice and would bring extra food along to give any children who didn't have much food in their lunch pail. This happened quite often, as it was the Great Depression of the 1930s, and many of the neighbors in the community couldn't sell their crops or livestock for enough money to live on.

Charlotte liked Miss Lindberg, and she was always the first in her class to get her work done. Miss Lindberg gave her extra work when she was finished, but Charlotte didn't mind. One day she told Charlotte to write the numbers one to five hundred. Charlotte became tired before she was through and scrawled the last numbers on the page. Miss Lindberg called her to her desk and told her, "Charlotte, this is very messy. You can do better than that, and I want you to do it over." Charlotte learned that though Miss Lindberg was kind, she expected her to do good work and do it right.

The desk that Marie and Charlotte sat in together was much too big for them. Miss Lindberg talked to the school board, who had promised Miss Krull they would bring some small desks from nearby Giddings School the year before. They promised Miss Lindberg too, but when they did not bring them, she got into her little car and drove over to Giddings School herself. She brought back two small desks, and the older children carried them into the schoolhouse. Charlotte and Marie sat in them, and the desks fit them perfectly.

"Oh, this is so nice," exclaimed Marie. "They fit just right. Now we can be in our own desks and our feet will touch the floor!" Miss Lindberg liked it too. She could arrange the children by grades, and that made it much easier for her. Charlotte liked her second-grade teacher very much and decided she would be a teacher just like her when she grew up.

THE BLACK SALVE

"We really had fun in school today," cried Pauline as they rushed in all together. "Teacher had a spelling bee, and my side won."

"That was because Charlotte and I were on your side," teased Clara. "We didn't miss one word."

"Hush, hush," said Ma. "George is asleep. I haven't been able to put him down all day, he's been so sick."

The children became silent and tiptoed into the bedroom where baby George lay. His face was flushed and he was rolling and tossing in his sleep. "What is the matter with him?" whispered Pauline.

"I don't know," said Ma. "He's been coughing and crying like his chest is hurting. I gave him a cool bath because he is hot, and I know he has a fever. I wish Daddy would get home. I think we need to take him to the doctor."

Daddy was working on the road and wouldn't be home until six o'clock. Ma sent all of the children out to do chores except Marie. She put her in the rocking chair and carefully put George on her lap. "If he fusses, rock him a little. I have to get the milk pails cleaned up, so Pauline and Clara can milk the cows. Charlotte will have to wash the dishes when she gets in with the firewood. He has been so sick, I haven't been able to do anything but feed Goldie and Ted some lunch."

George wasn't any better by the time Daddy got home. Pauline hurried out to tell him to go to the house right away, and she and Clara would feed and water the team and take their harness off. Daddy hurried to the house with a worried look on his face.

He rushed to the bed where George lay. Daddy felt his forehead and listened to him breathe. He said. "I think he is getting pneumonia. We have to take him to Harrold to see the doctor right away."

Ma didn't think she should go with him to Harrold, as Goldie and Ted were both small and the house had to be kept warm. Ma did not like to have the children tend fires without an adult in the house. "Pauline will have to go along and hold him," she said.

She dressed George up warmly and wrapped a big blanket around him. Daddy went out to start the car and Pauline changed her clothes and put on Ma's warm coat. Ma put George on Pauline's lap and tearfully watched them drive out of the yard and up the hill.

When bedtime came, Clara helped Ma put Ted and Goldie to bed, then she, Marie and Charlotte stayed up with Ma because she was so upset. "I just know he has pneumonia," Ma said. "I hope Doctor Martin can do something about it."

It was late when they finally saw the headlights come down over the hill. They all waited anxiously by the door when Daddy stopped the car by the doorstep. Ma rushed out while he opened the passenger side door. He pulled George's blanket over his face, took him off Pauline's lap and put him into Ma's arms. "I'll be in after I get the car parked," he said. Pauline got stiffly out and followed Ma and George, who was asleep, into the house.

"He's pretty sick," said Pauline, "but the doctor gave us some medicine and some salve. Daddy has it in his pocket."

Daddy came in with a small sack in his hands. There was a bottle and a little round silver tin inside it. "The bottle has medicine to help his cough, if we can get him to take it," Daddy said. He took a flat packet out of his pocket. "This is waxed paper. We are supposed to put this salve on his chest, cover it with waxed paper, and then put a warm cloth over it. Doctor Martin put it on his chest right away after we got there. He has pneumonia. If this doesn't help by morning, we have to take him to Pierre to the hospital." Daddy and Ma were both worried. Pneumonia was a very bad sickness for anyone who caught it, especially babies, and there was little that could be done for it in the days before antibiotics were discovered.

The next morning George was fussy, but Ma and Daddy both thought he looked a little better. Everybody had been up late the night before, so Ma woke the school children a little later, as Daddy was going to stay home and would do the morning chores.

Once school was out, the children rushed home. They rushed over to the baby bed and though George was still pale, he gave them a little smile. "He's better!" cried Charlotte. "Oh, I was so worried about Georgie Porgie."

Ma smiled. "He is a lot better. I got him to eat some oatmeal, and he's been nursing me, too. I have to put some more salve on him, and you can watch me."

"Ugh," Marie exclaimed when Ma opened the little silver box. "That salve smells awful."

"I don't know what's in it," said Ma as she spread the black stuff on his chest, "but it is making him better. It isn't the medicine in the bottle, because I can't get him to take it. He just spits it out."

George was soon laughing and cooing and acting like his usual happy self. The black salve had made a very sick little boy well again. Doctor Martin became famous throughout the area in the 1930s, before antibiotics were ever heard of, for the lives he saved with his black salve.

Picking Up Cow Chips

"Everybody put on your coats and caps," Daddy called out. "We are going to pick up cow chips today."

"Cow chips!" exclaimed Clara. "Why?"

"We might run short on wood for the heating stove," explained Daddy. "I can't afford to buy any coal this year, so we'd better have a pile of cow chips to burn just in case we need them."

"I hope not," said Ma. "I hope not, too," said Daddy, "but they'd better be picked all the same."

Daddy already had the team, Rosie and Bob, hitched up to the wagon. Bob was a bigger, stronger horse than his predecessor, Vixen, and better for heavy work. Daddy had also remodeled the wagon, which originally had a single box with iron brackets on each side so a wide board the same length could be slipped into them, making what was called a double box. Daddy had put an extension on the brackets on one side and slipped another board into it to create a triple box, and it seemed very high to the smaller Uecker children. When Daddy picked corn, he made the box three boards high on one side and two on the other. He tossed the corn in so it would hit the top board on the triple box side and fall down into the wagon. When the load reached the top of the double box, that was all it would hold, and he would take it to the corncrib. He had fixed the box the same way to haul cow chips.

Daddy lifted Marie, Charlotte, and Ted into the wagon. Then he, Clara, and Pauline climbed in. He picked up the reins, giving them a little shake, and Rosie and Bob, who knew that meant he was ready to go, started to trot down the road.

"Where are we going?" asked Pauline.

"We're going to the pasture where John Gerlt had his cows last year. I've already asked him," answered Daddy, "and he said we could go ahead. He said I could cut the dead trees out down there too." He pointed to a big ravine full of trees. "But I'm going to start on a new job helping build a road for the county board next week, and I may not have time to get enough wood cut for the winter. I hope I can," he went on, "because Ma really hates to burn cow chips, and I don't blame her. But I thought we'd better gather a few loads. They make a lot of heat, and will come in handy in a pinch. When I get that road job done, I'll get Uncle Ted to help me clear a road to the ravine, so I can start cutting those dead trees out."

Soon they reached the pasture and Daddy stopped the team, wrapping the reins around the wooden standard at the front of the box. He jumped out and started lifting the smaller children out, while Clara and Pauline climbed out by themselves. He took the pitchfork out of the wagon. "I'll turn the cow chips over with the fork," he said, "and you kids pick them up and toss them into the wagon. Don't throw them too hard or they'll break," he warned. "If you break them, they will crumble when you pick them up to carry them to the house, and they won't burn as well either."

Daddy took the fork and started turning over chips. Pauline, Clara, and Marie, making faces at the smell, started picking them up to toss into the wagon. Ted and Charlotte were too young to pay any attention to the smell of cow chips. They thought it great fun and started sailing chips into the wagon.

"Not so hard, you two," warned Daddy. "I said easy, so they won't break. And you other three, get going. They don't smell that bad when they are real dry, just when you burn them, and burning them is better than freezing when the weather gets cold."

The children soon learned to throw the chips into the wagon without breaking them. They learned that if the chips just touched the triple board on the wagon box, they would fall gently down into the wagon. When the chips made a pile on the triple side, they would start filling the box on the double side. They all worked quickly, and by the time Daddy got all the chips turned over near the wagon, the children would have them all thrown in. Then Daddy would drive the team over to another spot where there were lots of cow chips, and they would start all over again. When the wagon was full, Daddy made a space in front and put the younger ones in. Then he, Clara and Pauline carefully climbed in beside them. He cautioned the children not to move around, because sitting or standing on the chips would break them. He shook the reins and said, "Giddap!" and Rosie and Bob started on a slow trot toward home.

Daddy stopped the wagon a short distance from the house and they unloaded the cow chips against a small shed that stood near the house. "We'll put the last load in the shed," Daddy said, "so it will be dry. If we use them, we'll replace them with the ones outside so they will be dried out when we are ready to use them. Meanwhile, I'll cover them with straw. This old shed has lots of cracks in the walls, so the wind will blow through to dry the chips out when we put them in."

The older children looked at each other and groaned. That meant that they would have to get more loads. Ted and Charlotte didn't care. They thought it was great fun to sail the chips into the wagon, and they were all ready for Daddy to put them back into the wagon to go after the next load.

When the second load was brought in, Ma called them into the house to eat a meal of potatoes, salt pork, gravy and best of all, fresh biscuits and butter. The children were hungry as they had done a good deal of walking in the clear fresh air. "Eat all you can," encouraged Daddy. "I want to get two more loads: then we will call it a day."

By the time they were done with the third load, Ted was tired and cranky, so Daddy sent him to the house. "How about you, Charlotte?" he asked. Charlotte shook her head firmly to signify *no*. If he wouldn't send Marie in, she wouldn't go either. She was almost as old as Marie and just as big. She decided that if Marie, Clara and Pauline could help get another load, she could, so Daddy lifted both Marie and her into the wagon while Clara and Pauline tiredly climbed in.

"You are so stubborn," whispered Marie to Charlotte. "If you had said you were tired, maybe I would have gotten to stay home too." Charlotte nodded soberly as she whispered back, "So is everybody else tired. I guess we'd better help, so we can all get done sooner." Marie thought it over and said, "You're right. I didn't think about it that way, but I suppose Daddy is as tired as we are. He has done the most walking and the most work of all."

"This will be a smaller load," promised Daddy, who had noticed for some time that he had four tired little girls. "We'll just pick up this bunch of chips that are against the fence and go home. I noticed them all close together when we hauled in one of the other loads and decided we'd save the easiest for the last." He drove the team over by the fence, jumped out and started turning the chips over with his fork. The girls climbed out, encouraged that this load wouldn't take as long, and started sailing chips into the wagon as fast as he turned them over. By that time, they were experts at throwing them in at a speed that was fairly fast but still wouldn't break them when they hit the side of the wagon box. When Daddy called out that they were through, they all climbed back into the wagon and were surprised to see that the load was nearly as large as the others. The team trotted gaily home, because they seemed to know it was the last load too, and pulled up in front of the small shed. Daddy and the two older girls put the load into the shed and Charlotte and Marie picked up the stray chips and put them on the pile beside the shed.

Everybody was tired, but the team had to be unhitched, watered and fed, and the chores had to be done. Ma surprised them, though. She had milked the cows and had put the milk through the cream separator. The smaller children had filled the wood box. All that was left to be done was to care for Rosie and Bob, feed the calves the skimmed milk from the separator, and fill the water pails on the washstand that stood by the kitchen door. Clara stayed in the house to help Ma put supper on the table. Marie and Charlotte fed the milk to the calves and filled the water pails. Daddy and Pauline took care of the horses, fed and watered the milk cows, and put the calves into the shed.

Charlotte and Marie were very tired. Marie went to sleep at the table before she had finished her supper, and Charlotte followed Daddy as he carried her into the bedroom. She woke Marie up enough so she could help her put on her nightgown, then put her own on. They both fell into bed and were soon sound asleep.

That winter, Charlotte found out why Ma didn't like to burn cow chips. One very cold day they ran out of wood, so Ma sent her and Ted after a basket of them. They ran out to the shed and filled the basket as fast as they could. They wanted to see how well the chips would heat the house. They carried them in, and Ma opened the heater door and put some in.

Charlotte loved the old heater. It was a beautiful stove that stood almost as tall as Daddy's shoulder. On the shiny top were four lion's heads with manes on them, each looking a different direction. The heater had a large door with twelve small ising-glass windows that showed the flames dancing within, reflecting them on the walls in the twilight before the lamp was lit. On each side of the door was a shiny piece of metal with lion heads and feet. The stove sat on a base made of the same-colored metal. The base had four squatted legs attached to it. Each leg had another lion head with its mane connected to the base, and a big paw was carved where it touched the floor.

"We won't throw very many cow chips in at a time," said Ma. "They'll smother the fire if we do, and then they'll really smell." She took the basket from the children and carefully put the dried chips into the stove. When they caught fire, the odor of burning manure filled the room.

"What's that awful smell?" asked Marie as she came in from the well with a pail of water.

"Cow chips," said Goldie wrinkling her nose. "They don't smell, they stink."

Goldie was right. The smell clung to the curtains, the children's clothes, their coats and caps, and a light dust would gather on everything in the house when the cow chips were burned. Ma spent a good deal of time airing out the house and airing clothes on the clothes line, but the dried cow chips did make a good steady heat and the pile was nearly all gone when spring arrived.

Many years later, after Charlotte had grown up, married, and her children were grown, the neighboring towns on their celebration days would have buffalo or cow chip-throwing contests. They gave prizes to the man, woman, and child who could throw a chip the greatest distance.

Charlotte belonged to an artist's club in Pierre, and she and other members of the club had set their easels up among the trees along the riverbank to paint pictures of the scenery on Farm Island. Before Charlotte set up her painting equipment, she spied a cow chip near her easel. She picked it up and sailed it toward an old stump in the distance to see if her aim was still true. She glanced up to see the group she was with looking at her in astonishment. "You should enter the women's division in the chip throwing contest," one of her companions told her.

"Not me," said Charlotte. "I gathered cow chips several years for real, and the only time I did it for kicks was when I was very young and my Daddy let me have my fun. After that, we did it by ourselves, and it was hard work. And every time I throw one, I think of how they smelled when we had to use them to heat the house in the wintertime."

She went back to her easel and began painting with a thoughtful look on her face, remembering the blue sky, the white clouds, the crisp autumn air, the horses stomping their feet and jingling their harness. She remembered the creaking wagon wheels, the prairie chickens flying up when they got too close, the children laughing and talking, and the thud of the cow chips as they fell gently against the bang board, then down into the wagon box. Those were sights and sounds that were dear to her heart, and she didn't want it spoiled by watching a noisy, jostling crowd with yelling contestants drowning out the carnival sounds while they jokingly tried their hand to see who could throw a chip the greatest distance down the hot, busy street.

Milk Soup

It was a cold, windy, dusty November day when the Uecker children arrived home from school. They rushed through the door pushing and shoving, laughing and talking.

"I'm hungry!" Ted exclaimed. "Do you have something to eat, Ma?"

"No," Ma said shortly, and she put some firewood into the stove. "We are just about out of wood, and I want you and Charlotte to get the wood box filled right away."

All of the children regarded Ma in astonishment. She usually greeted them with a smile, and most of the time she would give each of them a half slice of bread spread with peanut butter.

"We didn't have very much lunch in our pails today," said Clara. "He's probably pretty hungry."

"I know," said Ma soberly, "and I'm glad it's Friday, too. I don't know what I could have put in them if there had been another school day this week." She lined the pails in a row under the shelf in the kitchen cupboard.

One was a small syrup pail. That pail belonged to Ted. He was in the first grade at Crocus Hill School, and he and the other beginners sat near the stove. The older children sat closer together near the back of the room. Pauline and Marie shared a gallon syrup pail, and Pauline always had trouble getting the lid pried off. Clara and Charlotte shared the battered lard pail, and sometimes when it was windy, like today, the lid would pop off on their way to or from school and go sailing over the prairie, with Charlotte running frantically after it.

All three pails were empty now. All the children had had for lunch that day was one slice of bread apiece, with just a little bit of peanut butter spread over the top.

It was nearly dark, and Daddy still was not home. He had left early that morning with the wagon and team of horses to go to Blunt to see if he could borrow a few dollars from his brother Dave to tide the family over until he could find a job somewhere. It was the Great Depression, and Daddy and everyone else in the community were having a hard time trying to make a living for their families.

Marie stayed in the house to help Ma with the little children while Ted and Charlotte went out to the woodpile to get wood to fill the big box that sat behind the kitchen stove. Pauline and Clara each took a milk pail and went to the barn to feed and milk the cows. Brindle and Roanie were going dry and Tennessee and Jersey, the other two milk cows, had not had their new calves yet, so there wouldn't be much milk.

"Well, at least we have some," sighed Ma, when they brought the pails that were hardly half full to the house. "But I just don't know what else to have for supper." She had waited until pitch dark before she lit the lamp, because there wasn't much kerosene left in it. Ted and Charlotte carried the water to the house from the well down by the big cottonwood that stood on the creek bank. They carried it in gallon pails, which they poured into the big water pail that stood on the washstand. When they finished with that and had the wood box filled, their chores were done. Goldie sat on the pile of wood in the box, swinging her feet, kicking the box with her heels. "Don't do that," scolded Ma sharply. "You'll ruin your shoes!" But she really didn't mean it. She was just worried about what to have for supper.

Whenever Ma was worried, she told stories. "When I was a little girl back in Iowa," she began, "we had oyster stew in the wintertime. Your Grandpa would go to town and bring back a big pail of them. Your Grandma would heat the milk in one pan and the oysters in another. Then she would put the oysters into the hot milk and bring them just to a boil, put some salt, pepper and butter in the stew, and oh, it was so good."

"Let's have some oyster stew," said Goldie, her dark blue eyes sparkling, and she kicked the wood box harder than ever. Ma thought aloud, "Well, we've got the milk..." Then she had an idea. There was still some flour left, though very little, and she had baking powder and salt. "Let's have imitation oyster stew!" she exclaimed, and she reached into the cupboard for a bowl.

Pauline and Clara came in with the milk, their faces rosy from the cold. "We are going to have 'mutashion' oyster stew," cried Goldie as she ran across the floor to meet them. "We're what?" exclaimed Pauline, who knew there was no such thing as an oyster in the house. "Oyster stew!" chorused the rest of the children. Ma looked sheepish while she strained the milk through a clean cloth into a pan. "I was just telling them about the oyster stew we had when I was little," she explained. Pauline was fourteen and Clara was twelve, and they could remember having oyster stew a few times. Ten-year-old Marie and eight-year-old Charlotte knew what oysters were, but they had no idea what they tasted like. Ted was six, Goldie was four, and George only two, and they had no idea what an oyster even looked like. Ma was expecting another baby in the spring, and she didn't even want to think about it right then, things looked so bleak.

"Well, I'm going to make imitation oyster stew," said Ma, "and you can tell me what you think of it." She took the bowl and set it in the center of the table. The big blue can that held the flour and sifter, and also served as a stool for one of the children to sit on at the table, was nearly empty, and she reached way down and scraped a big cup of flour from the bottom. "There's more than I thought there was," she said happily. She went to the cupboard that she and Daddy had made from orange crates, pulled aside the gingham curtain she had strung across them, and took the can of baking powder from the top shelf.

She measured a teaspoon of baking powder and sprinkled it on the flour that she had poured into the sifter. The children watched as she put a pinch of salt on it and sifted all of it into the bowl. "I don't have any shortening or eggs," she said, "but maybe a pinch of soda will help," so she added some of that too. There was a little cream that she had skimmed off the morning's milk, so she added it with some more milk to the mixture and stirred it lightly into a stiff dough. She took the big white enamel kettle that she used to make soup and set it on the stove. She filled it nearly full with milk.

She gave Clara a big spoon and told her to take a turn stirring the milk to a boil, and then Pauline could take her turn. Ma explained that the milk had to be stirred so it wouldn't burn because Ted and Charlotte had filled the stove with wood and the top of the kitchen range was very hot. Marie set the table. There were only three bowls, so Ma told her to put cups in the rest of the places and to put a spoon beside each one.

Once the milk was hot, Ma seasoned it with salt and pepper. There wasn't any butter, but Ma said that it was whole milk and that should make it taste real good. She took the dough mixture and dropped small teaspoons of it into the simmering milk until it was all gone. Then, she covered the pan with the lid and put it on the back of the stove where it wasn't as hot. "We have to wait twelve minutes so the dough balls will get done in the middle," she said. "If anyone takes the lid off, they will be soggy."

There wasn't any clock. George had knocked it off the stand by Ma and Daddy's bed and it had broken into pieces, so Ma and Daddy had to guess the time by the sun, and they did a good job of it too, as the children always got to school on time unless they were delayed by morning chores. "Let's sing some songs," said Ma. "When we get through with three songs, our imitation oyster stew will be done." So, they sang *The Cowboy's*

Lament, Marching Through Georgia, and *Pretty Red Wing* last, because it was everybody's favorite.

When all three songs were sung, Ma took the stew off the stove and everybody found their place at the table. Pauline sat on the small cream can. Clara sat on the flour can. Marie sat on the big cream can and Charlotte, Ted and Goldie sat on the high bench behind the table against the wall. Ma sat on her chair with George on her lap. Daddy's chair was empty. The family hoped he would soon be home, and they wanted his chair ready when he got there.

Ma dished out the stew, with Pauline and Clara staring at it skeptically. The rest of the children had so much faith in Ma that they started eating it at once. "It's good," said Charlotte. "I hope you made a lot." Pauline took a spoonful. "Why, it's dumplings!" she exclaimed, "little dumplings. I thought you needed lard and eggs for them."

"I do," confessed Ma, "when I have them." All of the children ate the imitation oyster stew, and they all thought it was delicious.

While the children were eating, they heard the creaking wheels of the wagon and the squeaking harness along with the hoof beats of the team clip-clopping on the frozen ground. It was Daddy, and he drove the team and wagon right up to the doorstep. Ma and the children were excited because they knew he had something to bring into the house, or else he would have driven straight to the barn to put the team up for the night. He came in stomping his feet, carrying a big box of groceries, then he went back to the wagon and carried in a fifty-pound sack of flour, went out again and brought a hundred-pound sack of potatoes in on his shoulder. "I scooped coal for six hours at the coal cars for that," he said proudly, "and there is a five-gallon can of kerosene for the lamps out there too. The coal cars came in just as I got to town and they needed someone to unload them right away, so I joined the other men that were on the car. Thank the good Lord I got there when I did."

Ma was so happy she whistled a tune while she put the small children to bed; then she, Clara and Pauline put the groceries away while Daddy unhitched and took care of the team. "I'm so glad!" Ma exclaimed. "I had really scraped the bottom of the barrel this time."

When Daddy came into the house, he took off his outdoor clothes and washed up. He said he wasn't hungry. He had eaten a meal at Uncle Dave's before he started for home, but Ma had heated up the leftover stew, so he said he would eat some of it while he told her about the trip. He sat down and looked at the bowl of stew suspiciously. "What's this?" he asked. "Oyster stew," announced Ted sleepily from his cot in the living room. Ma, Clara, and Pauline laughed. "So," said Daddy, "we really are doing great. We are even having oyster stew." He ate it all and winked. "Not bad. In fact, it's the best oyster stew I've had in a long time."

In later years, the family had it at least once a year, and they all looked forward to a real treat, for Ma could make a delicious oyster stew. And they also had imitation oyster stew, because they liked it so much. They called it Milk Soup.

The Garrigans

Back when the Uecker family lived on the Ditzler Place in Webster Township, Ma and Daddy became friends with the Garrigan family. There were two girls, Loretta and Nell, and five boys, Frank, John, Ray, Loren and Charles. John was called "Jack," and Charles was better known as "Red." Their father had died, leaving them with a small herd of cattle. Frank and Jack found a pasture in south Hyde County for the cattle, and their mother, Mary, moved to Highmore with the other children. It soon became apparent that, together with a neighbor or two, the people with whom they were pasturing were stealing the cattle one or two at a time. The Ueckers were on the Lamphere Place by then, and Frank and Jack rode their horses over to ask if Ma and Daddy could pasture their cattle. Their mother needed every cent she could get to provide for the smaller children, and they wanted to work with someone they could trust. Daddy told them he would pasture the cattle if he could milk some of the cows for their cream. They agreed to the

117

deal and drove their cattle to the Congdon Place once the Ueckers had moved there. They tried to get jobs in the surrounding area when they were available, and when they weren't, they slept in the Ueckers' haymow.

Times became very hard. Daddy would walk or ride the saddle horse to find jobs that would keep everyone fed. His meager paychecks were supplemented with the cream check which, because of low prices during the 1930s, was very small indeed. The Ueckers milked fourteen cows, and the calves had to be fed. But they were still better off than most, because there was milk for the children to drink.

Dust storms would shroud the valley in a yellow-gray fog and the Russian thistles would fly across the prairie and catch in fences, tearing them down. It seemed like the wind blew hard every day, churning up the dust, adding it to the dust that came in from the South. What few crops were left were eaten by the grasshoppers that came in droves, eating everything in their path. They stripped all the young leaves from the trees, ate the grain down to the ground, then chewed away the bark on the trees and the wood on the telephone poles and fence posts.

Loretta Garrigan became a good friend of Ma's. She taught rural school for several years before she married Everett Fuller, better known as "Bud." They'd had two small children when Loretta began having terrible headaches. Eventually, Loretta became so ill she needed continual care and the family moved to Highmore to live with her mother. Before she passed away, the Ueckers went to visit them, driving on the Reservation road past Big Bend through the ridge of hills called Chaney Rush.

The trip was memorable for Charlotte, who was nine or ten, because it happened when the grasshoppers were at their worst. They covered the rocks, fence posts, and telephone poles. The ground was stripped bare. The road ditches were filled with dust and in some places, only the tops of fence posts stood out. Grasshoppers stayed in the shade while they gnawed on the posts and poles, creating a spiral type indentation with hardly any chewing on the south side. This always left a small spire sticking up. Daddy stopped the car and told everyone to look, because they probably would never see anything like it again in their lifetime. And they never did.

Fifth Grade

Charlotte skipped the fourth grade, so she was eight years old when she started her fifth-grade year. She would be nine in November. She was small and wiry. Her hair was white. Her eyebrows and eyelashes were white. Her eyes were dark blue. Marie was in the fifth grade too. She had golden, curly hair and pretty blue eyes fringed with dark eyelashes. She was ten years old, and she was the oldest of the Uecker children going to Crocus Hill School that year. Ted was seven years old and in the second grade. Ted had curly blonde hair, mischievous blue eyes, and a big cheerful smile for everybody. Pauline and Clara had graduated from the eighth grade the year before. Now it was Marie, Charlotte, and Ted trudging their way to school down the little knoll where the house stood, through a small valley of trees, then up the long hill. At the top of the hill was the fence to be crawled through, then a short distance further north stood the schoolhouse with the schoolyard fence around it.

The other children going to school that year were the Cunningham children, the McMillan and Hall children, and Kathryn McCue. The Walter Hall children left early in the year, leaving Charlotte without a classmate. The teacher, Miss Byrum, had talked to Ma and Daddy about putting Charlotte in the fifth grade with Marie and Ralph McMillan. She said she was sure Charlotte was capable of doing fifth-grade work and then she wouldn't be alone in her class. Ma and Daddy gave their permission, and Charlotte felt proud to be in a class with the older pupils.

Miss Byrum loved children. There weren't any beginners that year, so Ted and Bobbie were still her little ones. She would put one on each knee during their reading class, and she grouped the others around her desk during their classes. Miss Byrum did not like having them sit on the Recitation Bench. She said they were too far away. She was a good teacher and because the children liked her so well, she never had any disciplinary problems.

That year of 1932-33 was one of the worst of the drought. There was no snow, and the wind blew every day. When the wind blew hard, the stove smoked, and soot would fly over the room. Miss Byrum would have to excuse school and the children would run home, glad to be out for the day. Finally, some members of the school board came early one Saturday morning and took the stovepipes down to clean them. They found that a big bird's nest had clogged the chimney. They cleaned it out, fixed the draft and washed the soot from the walls and curtains. School was held every day after that.

When the tumbleweeds started rolling across the prairie in the fall, Charlotte, Ted and Bobbie would race after them, hitting them with sticks to lift them over the fence. Then they would watch them bounce over the prairie until they were out of sight.

The children at Crocus Hill belonged to the Young Citizens League, a program designed to teach and practice citizenship in rural schools. The children had meetings and voted for officers. The officers selected committees. The committees were appointed to do various chores to keep the school clean and assist the teacher. The older ones carried in kindling and coal from the coal house and put hay in the mangers for the horses the children rode to school or hitched to carts.

They were also responsible for raising the flag on the pole that stood in the schoolyard. One of the children led the flag salute. After that, they sang the national anthem. Two of the pupils took the flag down after school, folded it carefully and put it away. In the wintertime, they would not raise the flag outside, but two children would hold the flag up for the salute in the schoolroom. Younger pupils were chosen to assist, so they would know how to do it properly when they reached the upper grades.

Other children swept the floor, cleaned the desks with a damp cloth, dusted, cleaned the blackboards and swept the outdoor toilets. The beginners dusted the erasers. This was all done after school. If the weather was bad, the chores were postponed and the teacher did the necessary duties. The teacher was responsible for starting the fire in the heating stove, taking out the ashes and keeping the school warm. She filled the water cooler with water brought by one of the parents and saw that the children washed their hands when they came in from the toilet and recess. She also saw that the lunch pails were put away, helped the smaller children with their winter clothes and made sure the fire was banked properly before she mounted her saddle horse to go to her boarding place at the Maines farm, nearly three miles away. This was not the end of her day, as she usually had all of the daily schoolwork to correct when she arrived home so she could hand it back with the corrections and advice the next day. School began at nine o'clock and ended at four, but a rural schoolteacher's day never ended until nearly bedtime.

Herding Turkeys

Charlotte and Ted did not like to herd turkeys. But after all was said and done, they had to do it, because nobody else liked to herd them either.

Ma would get out of bed when the sun came up and follow the turkeys when they ranged out to catch bugs. She would stay with them for about an hour, then go back to the house to wake Charlotte up. She would tell her where they were, and Charlotte would quickly dress and go to the hill where the turkeys made their first stop to catch insects and scratch for seeds for their breakfast.

The turkeys were the Uecker family's extra income. In the spring, Ma would start gathering eggs as soon as the hens began laying eggs in the nests they made near the creek. The eggs had to be gathered every day because the muskrats and skunks would steal them if they were left in the nest overnight. When Ma had gathered enough eggs, she and Daddy set up several triangle-shaped coops near the house to discourage the coyotes, who didn't like to come too close to the buildings. Whenever they tried, their dog Beans would make such a racket he would scare them away. Ma and Daddy fixed nests in the coops, put a setting of about fourteen eggs in each one, and then put the turkey hens in the coop. They nailed slats over the doorway so the hens couldn't get out, and put pans of food and water inside. At night, they would let the hens out to graze and exercise. By that time, the hens were broody and wanted to hatch their eggs, so they would go back into the coop without being coaxed.

There were always extra eggs, and Ma put them in a small brown incubator. It had a little kerosene lamp attached to it. The lamp was enclosed so the heat from it would enter the incubator through a small chimney. There was a thermostat on top to regulate the heat after Ma set it to correspond with the thermometer inside the incubator, which had to be 103 degrees. She put a small pan of water under the rack of eggs, then set the thermometer on top. The more even the temperature stayed, the better it was for the little turkeys developing inside the eggs. On the tenth day, she candled them by cutting a hole in a piece of cardboard, holding it in front of each egg and then holding the egg against the light from the kerosene lamp. If the egg was clear, it was discarded. If it had a round shadow with blood vessels coming out from the shadow, she knew it was the beginning of a little turkey. She never had to discard very many. There were small air holes placed on the sides of the incubator and there was a larger one on top that could be adjusted. She turned the eggs every day, and after the second week took the trays out of the incubator for a short time each day to cool down. She would place one of the children near the incubator to remind her to put the eggs back in after they were cooled.

The turkey hens hatched their little turkeys at nearly the same time as the incubator did. Ma and Daddy put some of the turkeys from the incubator with each of the hens, so they would have at least fifteen little turkeys apiece. Then Daddy would catch the gobbler and tie him by one leg to a small tree. In a few days, after the gobbler had gotten used to being tied and was eating grain and drinking water from the pans placed near him, Daddy would put the rest of the little turkeys from the incubator with him. He would move the gobbler every few days to a different location, always tying him to a stake. This kept him from striking at the small turkeys. In a week or so, when the gobbler was used to them, he would begin scratching for seeds and bugs for them to eat and at night, he would let them crawl under his feathers for warmth. When he had fully accepted the little turkeys, Daddy would put him and his adopted family with the hens, who by that time were ranging out to get feed for their little ones.

The turkeys made a lot of noise. If they saw something strange, they would gather around it, and the hens would cluck noisily. Then they would make a whirring sound, and the little turkeys would become very quiet and run to get underneath the hens and the gobbler for protection. The sad part was that the adult turkeys weren't very good at protecting the little ones. They would gather into a circle too close to the snake or skunk. Even though they would chase or peck, the skunk or snake could always dash in and take off with a baby turkey.

That was why Charlotte and Ted had to herd them. There were about two hundred and fifty small turkeys that had to be protected from skunks, snakes and hawks during the day and skunks and coyotes at night. All morning long Charlotte, with Beans for company, trudged after the turkeys as they foraged up the creek valley. At noon, she herded them back to the farm when it was time for dinner. After dinner, she and Ted, with a jar of water to drink and accompanied by Beans, would follow alongside the turkeys when they went up over the high hill south of the creek to forage for insects on the prairie. In the late afternoon, the turkeys would go back home to drink at the creek and dust themselves in the ash pile. It was a long day for a nine- and seven-year-old, and their bare feet became so calloused that cactus thorns had difficulty penetrating the skin.

Even so, one time when Charlotte was herding the turkeys through a plum thicket, she stepped on a thorn. It broke off in her foot and became embedded. Then she started to limp until finally, she could not step on it at all. She was hopping along with her other foot when Ma saw her and sent one of the older children out to herd the turkeys. Ma had her soak her foot in hot water several times a day. In a few days, Ma could see a dark spot, so she started squeezing gently to force the thorn out. The next day it flew out, and Charlotte was able to begin walking gingerly with both feet again. That was enough for the older girls: Charlotte's reprieve didn't last long. She was back out herding turkeys the next day.

The baby turkeys grew into young poults. Ma and Daddy praised Charlotte and Ted because very few had been lost. The turkeys had to be herded instead of being kept in pens because there was no money to buy feed for them until fall. They ate the bugs and grasshoppers around the garden and in the pasture, then would range out on the creek bottom. That was the most dangerous, as that was where the snakes and skunks hid out.

One early morning when Charlotte went out to herd the turkeys, she saw them bunched up in a circle gobbling, clucking and hissing. She saw a big blue racer snake slipping in to steal a little one. She picked up some rocks and hurled them at the snake, then started driving the turkeys back down the hill. While she was moving them along, she heard a hiss and turned her head to see the blue racer angrily moving on his tail, his head even with her shoulder. He was hissing and bobbing at her. Charlotte screamed, threw her stick down and ran to the house crying for Ma all the way. Ma was making breakfast, but when she heard Charlotte scream, she came rushing out on the step. When she finally found out what happened, she sent Pauline and Clara to get the turkeys and consoled Charlotte, who finally quit sobbing. Pauline and Clara had to herd the turkeys the rest of the morning.

At night, the turkeys roosted on a board fence and in the branches of a big box elder tree that stood near the edge of the creek. Every night, the howls of the coyotes came closer and closer, and Beans grew angrier and angrier. Charlotte and Ted tried to chase them up higher in the trees, but the turkeys would fly down to the lower branches as soon as they left. One morning, Daddy found some feathers on the ground where a coyote had grabbed a young one. After that, he gathered some poles and built roosts near the barn and every night, Charlotte and Ted had to drive the turkeys to roost on them.

That April, Ma had given birth to a new baby girl whom they named Florence Caroline after Uncle Ted's wife. She was born in Harrold with Dr. Martin and Dollie Hall assisting. While Charlotte and Ted herded turkeys, Marie helped Ma by taking care of baby Florence.

When school started, Ted and Charlotte were happy to go. School meant they didn't have to herd gobbling, noisy turkeys all day long. Daddy told Pauline and Clara, who were out of grade school, to take charge. They took turns herding them with Buster the saddle horse, but as soon as school was out and the children were home, Ted and Charlotte were back herding the turkeys on foot again.

In October, advertisements to buy turkeys came in the mail. One of the advertisements was from the nine Fox brothers from Chicago. There were nine gobblers on the ad with a picture of each of the Fox brothers and their names in place of the turkey heads. They gave a good price, and Daddy and Ma decided to ship the turkeys there. Daddy started feeding them a mixture of corn and oats, and the turkeys grew big, fat and shiny. Two weeks before Thanksgiving, Daddy, Ma, Pauline and Clara dressed them out to ship. Charlotte and Marie had the job of placing paper bags over their heads and tying the bags on before the turkeys were placed in wooden crates and the lids were fastened down. Jack and Frank Garrigan came to help load them up in their cars and they took them to the Harrold train depot, where they shipped them to Chicago.

Ma and Daddy got a good price for the turkeys and used some of the money to order new shoes for the children. Daddy chose laced high-top boots with a small pocket that snapped shut on the side of one boot for Marie, Ted and Charlotte. He said Marie had earned them for watching Florence for Ma all summer, and Ted and Charlotte for herding the turkeys every day.

The Hailstorm

Ma didn't like storms. When she was a child growing up near Ree Heights, a bad one came up and destroyed all their buildings but the house, and storms had frightened her ever since. She was glad the cellar on the place on Chapelle Creek was a good one and close to the house. The house was surrounded by hills on the north, east and south sides, and there was a small prairie to the west with hills beyond it, making it hard to see storm clouds gathering. So when a storm came up, the family really had to hurry for shelter. Ma watched any menacing cloud that came into view very closely, and she always managed to get the family into the cellar before it arrived, except once.

One night in early August, there were no clouds in sight when the family went to bed. Daddy was sick, and he had gone to bed earlier than the rest. Sometimes Daddy got bad stomachaches and could not work. It wasn't until years later, when he was rushed to the hospital in Pierre for emergency surgery, that the family realized his bad stomachaches were actually appendicitis attacks.

On this particular night, the rest of the family had done all the chores. Ma, Pauline and Clara milked the fourteen cows and ran the milk through the cream separator, while Marie watched the younger children and kept them quiet so Daddy could sleep. Ted and Charlotte carried in the wood for the cook stove and filled the water pails. They chased the half-grown turkeys into the upper branches of the trees. They had to do this every night, so the coyotes couldn't reach them when they came sneaking up the creek.

Once the milk was separated, the children fed the calves while Ma and the older girls got supper. They ate their meal quietly by lamplight, hoping Daddy could sleep until his stomachache was better.

Ma put the younger children to bed while the older ones washed and dried the dishes. Then she sent everyone to bed even though the weather was very hot and usually, everyone went outside and talked when the work was done. On this night, Ma wanted no noise at all as Daddy had been in pain when he went to sleep, and she wanted him to rest.

Just before midnight, Ma woke up. She heard a peculiar roaring noise that frightened her. She nudged Daddy from his fitful sleep and told him to listen. Daddy had heard a roar like that before. He told Ma to get the children to the cellar and do it immediately. Ma looked out the window and cried, "It looks like a white wall is coming, and it's nearly here!" She shouted, "Everybody awake, and get to the cellar!"

The children sprang from bed dazed by sleep and started for the door. Ma urged Daddy to come along, but Daddy had such a severe stab of pain when he sat up that he roared, "Get out of here, and get to the cellar, now!" Ma told Marie and Charlotte to get the younger ones and she and Clara and Pauline tried to lift Daddy up to help him. He nearly screamed with pain. He fell back on the bed and roared again, "Get to the cellar! I'll be all right." Ma started pushing everybody to the door then, but the storm hit, so they couldn't open the door. Then the north window in the kitchen flew inward, shattering the glass onto the floor.

"You kids get in here!" Daddy shouted from the bedroom, and Marie and Charlotte pushed the little ones into the bedroom. He reached out with his big hands and slid them under the bed. By that time, Ma and Pauline and Clara had shoved a mattress up against the hole where the window had been, to stop the hail and rain from pouring in. Marie and Charlotte started sweeping up the glass and hail. Ma was very scared, but she stayed calm and ordered them out of the kitchen while she and the older girls braced themselves against the mattress to keep it in the window hole.

The storm finally passed over and when they all looked outdoors, they gasped. "How bad is it?" asked Daddy weakly. "The ground is all covered with hail," answered Ma, "and it is still raining."

"The turkeys and calves!" exclaimed Daddy, trying to get up again, and again he fell back in pain.

"Stay right there," Ma said firmly, and turned to Marie and Charlotte. "Put the little ones back in bed, and then get the fire going in the cook stove. Pauline, you and Clara come with me." And they went outside into drifts of hail and rain.

Charlotte and Marie looked at each other in amazement. "It's already too warm in here," Marie said, "but we'd better do what she says." They put kindling in the firebox in the kitchen range, and it lit up from live coals in the box.

The fire was burning and the oven was warm when Ma and the older girls made their first trip back to the house with as many half-grown turkeys as they could carry. "Rub them good with a towel, put them in the oven on an old coat, and leave the oven door open," she ordered. "But they're dead!" exclaimed Marie. "Do as I say," ordered Ma again, and the door slammed behind them. Marie and Charlotte dried the turkeys the best they could with an old towel and laid them on the coat they had placed in the oven. All of a sudden, one of them started to kick. "They were knocked out by the hail!" exclaimed Charlotte.

The girls were encouraged by the first kick, and set to work with a will. The first turkey shook its head and stood up with a feeble peep, then another started moving his legs, and soon they were all standing up, chirping and trying to get away. Charlotte emptied the wood out of the tall wood box, and they put the turkeys in that. By that time, Ma and the older girls had made another trip with their hands full, carrying the turkeys by the legs. They had waded through the water and hail to put all of the other turkeys that were dazed, but still struggling in the cold water into the barn, then they brought the ones that were unconscious to the house. Next, they went to the calf pen and chased the dazed calves into the shed. By that time, the creek was roaring from all of the water that had poured into it from the cloud-burst and hail, so they knew they couldn't cross it to check on the cows.

"They'll be all right after the storm," said Daddy. "Just get those wet clothes off and get dry, or you'll all be sick." Clara and Pauline were shivering and crying.

Their feet were bruised and cold from walking barefoot through the hail.

Ma sent everyone to bed. She braced the mattress more firmly against the hole in the wall, and then did more toweling on the turkeys that were in the house. There were nearly thirty of them, and they saved all but three of them. That fall, there were still over two hundred and fifty turkeys remaining when they shipped them to the Fox Bros. Co. in Chicago, Illinois. The money from that sale would be the only income the Ueckers would have besides the cream check for the rest of the year.

The morning after the storm, Daddy was weak, but he felt better. The creek was high for a little while, but by noon the cows could swim across to be milked.

There were piles of hail lying all around. Daddy told the children to put buckets of it under the hay in the haystack so they could make some ice cream to celebrate. Thanks to Ma and the children, they had come through with all of the livestock safe and well, and they were grateful.

"But we don't have an ice cream freezer," complained Ted. "I'll show you how it's done," promised Daddy. "Just wait until tomorrow, when I feel better. I'll fix the window with boards until we can get some glass, then I'll show you."

The next day, Ma mixed up enough ice cream mix to fill a gallon syrup pail nearly to the top. She was just as curious as the children to see what came next. Daddy put some hail in the bottom of a milk pail, then some salt. He put the top firmly on the pail of ice cream mix and placed it in the center of the milk pail, then filled the pail with alternating layers of hailstones and salt until the layers nearly covered the lid. He picked up the handle of the syrup pail and turned it back and forth, forward and back, for several minutes. He took the lid off and with a knife, scraped the ice cream from the sides, then put the lid back on and turned again, taking the lid off at intervals and scraping the sides down. In a short while, the bucket was full of delicious ice cream. Then he put the lid firmly back on and covered it with hail and salt. Ted was disappointed. "I thought we were going to eat it," he said. "We will," said Daddy. "It has to set awhile to get firm. Get your dishes and spoons ready. It won't be long."

Their nearest neighbor, John Gerlt, came over to see if everybody was all right. Charlotte ran and took him by the hand. "You are just in time for some hail ice cream!" she cried. "Ma and Daddy made it!" John looked at her curiously, and Ma and Daddy laughed and explained how they had done it.

Soon they were eating the ice cream and they all agreed it was very good. Ma said she wished she could have put a couple more eggs into it, but that was all she had. "Is there any hail left?" asked John. "Lots of it," answered Pauline. "We covered it with hay."

"I'll go home to get some eggs," said John, "if your folks will make some more." Daddy nodded his head, so he went back home over the hill with Ted and Charlotte hanging onto his hands, chattering to him about the storm. They went into the house where John got a can of sugar off the shelf and gave it to Charlotte to carry. "If your folks furnish the milk and cream, I'll furnish the sugar and eggs." He picked up a pail of eggs, and they went back over the hill to fix another "pail of hail ice cream."

Sixth to Eighth Grade

Charlotte was in the sixth grade when Miss Zetta Loughlin started teaching Crocus Hill School. She was small,
slim, brown-haired and gray-eyed. She drove a Model
A Ford car and boarded at the schoolhouse. Her home
was in Blunt, where she lived with her mother and sister
Rose. She was Charlotte's teacher the rest of her years
at Crocus Hill School.

Miss Loughlin was firm and determined that each
child would pay attention in class. She was also very kind,
and it was not until later that the children fully realized
how much of herself she gave to each one of them. Her
pupils were John Gerlt's niece, Kathryn McCue, Rose
Cunningham, Marie and Charlotte Uecker in the upper
grades; Roberta (Bobbie) Cunningham and Ted Uecker
in the middle grades; and Melvin and Marjorie Cunningham and Goldie Uecker in the first grade.

Charlotte, Marie and Ted were ashamed of Goldie
because she would not talk. She was very small and very
timid. Miss Loughlin would ask Melvin and Marjorie,

who were twins, to count to ten, and they would. She would ask Goldie to count to ten, and she would say nothing, even though Goldie could count to one hundred at home. She would ask the twins to read from their primer, and they would. She would ask Goldie to read, and she would say nothing. All day long, she would not say a single word. But as soon as the children walked over the hill toward home, she would begin to talk and giggle. Each morning, Ted would ask, "Are you going to talk today, Goldie?" and Goldie would nod her head "yes," but when she got to school, she would be quiet as a mouse. She wouldn't even talk to Melvin or Marjorie, though she had always talked to them when the families visited with each other.

One day, after school had been open for over two weeks, Ma and Daddy left Florence with Pauline and Clara, who didn't go to high school that year because there was no money for their room and board. They went to Crocus Hill to see if they should keep Goldie out of school another year. Miss Loughlin replied, "Let her stay. She knows what is going on, and I can tell she understands what I am teaching. Give her time, and she will talk. I can see she wants to." Miss Loughlin almost gave up, though, when Goldie still wouldn't say a word six weeks after school started.

Until one day, Miss Loughlin asked Marjorie a question during arithmetic class, and she didn't know the answer. She asked Melvin the same question, and he couldn't answer either. Then she absently asked Goldie, and she *answered* correctly. All of the other children looked up in surprise. Then Marjorie and Melvin both shouted, "She talked! Goldie talked! Did you hear her?" Everybody laughed and from then on, Goldie talked.

The Cunningham children came to school in a cart drawn by a little roan mare named Roxie. Mr. Cunningham furnished the water for the school and put a five-gallon can of water in the cart each morning before he sent the children to school. Roxie was a nice little mare, but every so often she would get a stubborn streak after she was hitched up to go home, and she wouldn't budge no matter what was tried. The Uecker children would grab her by the bridle and try to pull her into the first step, but she wouldn't budge. If she took one step, she would come out of her balkiness. Sometimes they would re-harness her and put the side shafts in different positions, but she would still refuse to move. Miss Loughlin would come out to help, but she couldn't get Roxie to move either. Finally, with all of them coaxing, pulling and pushing, she would take a step. Then all the children would get out of the way, because she would take off in a fast trot for home.

Roxie didn't have many such stubborn streaks, though. The Uecker kids always helped Rose get her hitched up, then helped Bobbie and the twins into the cart with the water can, and they would be on their way home.

The schoolyard was covered with prairie grass with a few small irises in beds ringed with rocks. There were lots of gopher holes with gophers running in and out while the children played. There was a bounty of two cents apiece for every gopher tail that was brought in to the courthouse in Pierre, and Miss Loughlin said she would take them in for the bounty. So every now and then, the children went on a gopher hunt.

Miss Loughlin taught Crocus Hill School for three years. She was a good teacher and kept her children's interest with projects and awards for good work. The awards were presented on decorated parchment paper. She took the children on excursions outside the schoolyard, where they identified grasses, weeds and birds.

She encouraged class projects and required current events from the upper grades. She subscribed to a weekly school newspaper called *My Weekly Reader* so the children could keep up with current events and report what they read in class. She had spelling bees, which were popular, and math bees, which brought groans from most of the children: Charlotte was one of them.

On the last Friday of each month, the students held a Young Citizens League (YCL) meeting. The meeting was conducted by children in the upper grades. Charlotte was the president, Marie the secretary, and Rose the treasurer. Ted and Bobbie were on the Entertainment Committee. Charlotte, Marie and Bobbie were in charge of assigning the children their duties for the month, with Miss Loughlin as the supervisor. Miss Loughlin sat on a chair at the back of the room and contributed only when asked. For the most part, the meeting was conducted entirely by the students.

As president, Charlotte stood by the chair at the teacher's desk and announced, "The Crocus Hill School YCL meeting will come to order. We will now have the Flag Salute, and Goldie and Marjorie may hold the flag." After the flag salute, she said, "Now we will sing the Star-Spangled Banner." The students had no accompaniment, but they knew the anthem, and Marie and Bobbie led the singing. Then Charlotte said, "Now Marie will give the minutes to the last meeting, and Bobbie will give the treasurer's report."

After that, she asked for old business and then, new business. Any child who had business to discuss would stand and say, "Madam President." Charlotte would recognize the members by name. Then they would say,

"I make a motion to..." and present whatever they had in mind. Charlotte would ask for discussion and then would say, "The motion has been made and seconded concerning the subject. Are there any additions or corrections?" If there weren't any, she would ask all in favor to raise their right hand. Then she would ask all against the motion to raise theirs. If the motion carried, it was entered in the Secretary's book and obeyed for the rest of the term.

After the business meeting, they had entertainment: often a spelling bee, followed by a lunch. Ma would send milk to be heated on the teacher's small kerosene stove, the Cunninghams' grandmother would send cocoa and sugar, and Miss Loughlin would furnish a snack: either a couple of cookies or a dish of Jell-O. Afterwards, the children would go outside to play.

Miss Loughlin suggested the children should discuss whom they wanted for delegates to the YCL convention in Pierre. The delegates would sit at a desk at the Capitol with the Senator from Hughes County and watch the legislature conduct its meeting. This was a day set aside for all YCL delegates from all the counties. The Crocus Hill YCL chose Charlotte and Marie to be their delegates. They were allowed thirty cents apiece from the treasury to spend on their trip to Pierre to visit the legislature. Miss Loughlin took them to Pierre and brought them home again.

Miss Loughlin also took all of the children on an excursion to Pierre as a special treat. She took them to the parks and over the bridge to Fort Pierre to see the fence Scotty Phillips, "the man who saved the buffalo," had built to keep the buffalo on the range when he was trying to protect them from being finished off by hunters.

She also took them to the State Capitol Building. They went up to the Capitol Dome and looked out of the windows over the town. They visited the Governor's Office and the legislative chambers. The mosaic floor of the Capitol building has tiny blue tiles scattered throughout, and she waited while the children located all of them. Then she found a guide to take them through the tunnel to the Lake.

They used their "gopher money" to buy food for their lunch and took it to the park to eat. Then it was time to go, so she drove her tired pupils back to their homes. It was a long trip, as Pierre was more than thirty miles from Crocus Hill School and back then, none of the roads were paved.

Chasing Tumbleweeds

The fall of 1934 was a dirty, windy time. No rain had fallen for months. Every day, the wind blew clouds of ugly yellow dust over the prairie. The dust was everywhere, and even Mrs. Hanson, the Cunningham children's grandmother who was very particular with her housework, had given up. She cleaned each room thoroughly every morning but by noon, the windowsills were full of dust and little rivulets of it would settle onto the floor. Rose, Bobbie and Marjorie used the homestead shack that sat in their yard to play house with pots, pans and other utensils. But it wasn't fun to play house when the dust was forever blowing into their eyes, so they hung up the pots and pans.

The Uecker family's house was snuggled on the creek among the trees in a natural bowl surrounded by hills, so the wind did not blow as hard there. Still, the yellow dust filtered gently down and settled on the ground, the livestock, and the children when they went outside to play. Their hands, feet, faces and blonde hair would get so grimy with dirt that they would beg Ma to let them go into the pool by the spring so they could wash themselves. That helped to keep them clean until the weather became too cold. After that, Ma cut kerchiefs out of an old skirt for the girls to wear on their heads to protect their hair. Sometimes the dust was so thick, the barn would look like it was in a dense fog and the hills surrounding the creek could barely be seen.

When school started in September, the children trudged up the road over the hill where they met the wind blowing wildly on the prairie, carrying swirls of dirt down the cow paths. Marie, Charlotte, Ted and Goldie bent into the wind carrying their lunch pails, their sweaters and jackets flying out behind them. When they reached the schoolhouse and entered the hall, their teacher Miss Loughlin would say sharply, "Please, close the door." She tried to keep the schoolroom tidy, but it was nearly impossible with all the dust blowing everywhere.

The frost came in late September, and the Russian thistles covered the fields and bare spots on the prairie where the grass wouldn't grow. Charlotte liked to look at the thistles when they were green. They had beautiful tiny rose-colored flowers in every spine. *Like little doll flowers*, Charlotte thought, but when she touched them, she would pull her hand back in pain, for the spines were sharp as needles.

Soon after freezing, the thistles turned from their green color to an ugly black. Then after a short while, they turned to a light tan. After they turned tan, the wind blew them off their roots and they would go rolling over the prairie. Huge round thistles rolled everywhere, bouncing high into the air, hitting the fences, stretching the wires and sometimes breaking off posts, piling high only to be blown loose again when the wind changed direction.

The children at Crocus Hill School would have fun with the thistles that blew into the big schoolyard. They would take sticks and run behind them, hitting them to roll them faster over the ground. When they got to the fence, they would put their sticks underneath to lift them over, and the thistles would bounce again merrily over the prairie.

Sometimes, the entire school—Rose, Marie, Charlotte, Ted, Bobbie, Melvin, Marjorie and Goldie— would crawl through the fence and follow them. But the wind would give the whirling thistles so much momentum that soon they would outdistance the shouting, laughing children running and waving their sticks. Then they would then go back into the schoolyard and wait for more thistles to come bouncing over the fence.

Their teacher, Miss Loughlin, had visited the County Superintendent's Office in Pierre before school started. She was given some new reading books for the fourth grade. Ted and Bobbie were in the fourth grade and liked their new books. One day, they read about some children in a big city. The book showed a picture of a beautiful little girl in a pink dress, white socks, and black patent leather shoes chasing a hoop with a stick. "Oooh," exclaimed Bobbie. "I wish I had a hoop."

"That would be fun," said Marie when she looked at the picture, and all the rest of the children agreed. All but Charlotte, who said, "I don't think I'd want one."

"Oh, Charlotte," scolded Marie, "you always have to be opposite."

Charlotte said nothing and reached for her arithmetic book, but Miss Loughlin was curious. "Why wouldn't you want a hoop, Charlotte?" she asked.

Charlotte looked up. She brushed her dusty white hair away from her eyes. "I'd rather chase thistles with a stick," she answered. "They are just as round, and I'll bet they go faster. Besides..." She stopped, opened her book and reached for her pencil. "Besides, what?" demanded Bobbie. "Besides," said Charlotte, "you would always have to go get the hoop and put it away when you were through playing with it, so you could find it next time. When you play with thistles, you can chase them until you are tired, and then you can let them go. There are always a lot more when you want to do it again." Then Charlotte took her tablet out of her desk, bent her head, and began working on her arithmetic.

The Christmas Tree

"This isn't our year to have the school Christmas tree," said Charlotte.

"Yes, it is," Ted insisted. "We didn't have it last year."

"We did two years ago," said Marie. "Then Halls got it, and this year is Cunninghams' turn. Everybody else has moved away, so it will be our turn next year."

Daddy had told them he couldn't afford to buy a Christmas tree this year, and Ted was very disappointed. "Can't we cut down one of our own cedar trees?" he begged.

"No," said Ma firmly. "We need them to keep the wind and snow away from the buildings." "Besides," said Charlotte, "they are full of little blue berries, and the birds like them. That's all they'll get for Christmas."

"I wish we had something," said Marie when they went outside to do the chores. She kicked disgustedly at a big thistle that a small gust of wind had sent rolling across the yard. She looked at it for a moment, then she shouted, "We'll use a thistle for a tree!" Ted and Charlotte stared at her in amazement. "A thistle," said Ted. "Are you crazy? They are just weeds." But Marie was determined to try it. She went down the fencerow and picked out a big round thistle that had a little peak at the top of it. She pulled it out and walked to the house dragging the thistle behind her.

"Watch her come right back out with it," said Charlotte, but she was mistaken. Marie came out of the house with a lard pail and went down to the creek. She filled the pail with sand and returned to the house. "I've got to see this!" exclaimed Ted, so Charlotte, Ted and Goldie grabbed up their armfuls of stove wood and rushed to the house. They found Ma and Marie pulling the bottom spines from the big tan thistle. Ma set it into a pail, and she and Marie packed the sand around it firmly.

"We'll set it right here on the table," said Ma, "and when you get it decorated we will put it on the organ to keep it from the smaller children." Ted, Goldie, and Charlotte were enthusiastic by that time and hurried to find material to decorate the thistle. Ted and Goldie cut strips of paper to color while Ma made paste from flour and water. "Don't color the ends," cautioned Charlotte, "or they won't stick together when we make the chains." "Make the strips real small," said Marie. "This will be a small tree."

"You mean thistle," corrected Ted, as he pulled the flour can up to the table so he could sit on it while he cut paper strips. While they were making the chains, Ma went to the cupboard to get some pieces of tinfoil she had been saving. She rolled the pieces into small balls. She and Marie put string in a big needle and threaded it through the balls so they could tie them to the make-believe tree. Charlotte went to get a red ribbon that had been on her last year's Christmas present from Miss Loughlin. She had kept it neat and clean because it was so pretty. Now she cut it into short fine strips and hung them on the thistle. When they were through decorating it with the chains, foil balls and ribbon, it looked very nice, and the children all agreed that it was almost as good as a real Christmas tree.

"I heard about a lady making a Christmas tree from a thistle years ago," said Ma. "I'm glad you thought of it, Marie. It looks very nice, and it is a good substitute for an evergreen."

There was one small chain left and Charlotte still had two small strips of red ribbon in her hand. "Can I have these?" she asked. "I don't care," Ma answered. "You can do with them what you like." Charlotte went outside to the woodpile. Daddy was busy chopping wood, but he stopped briefly to see what she wanted. "Do you see that broken branch up there?" she asked, pointing to one of the cedar trees that stood on the north side of the house. Daddy looked up and saw a small branch about a foot long with tiny blue berries on it. It was broken off the main branch, perhaps by a turkey trying to perch on it. "Can I have it?" she asked. Daddy reached up and finished breaking the branch from the tree and handed it down to her. She took it into the house and put it on the table. "Please don't burn this," she told Ma. She went back outside, and found a tin can in the junk pile. She went to the creek, filled it with wet sand and returned to the house. After she put the chain and ribbons on the branch, she placed it in the can and carefully placed it behind the thistle tree where it could barely be seen.

"What did you do that for?" asked Ted. "You can't see it. It's a good thing, too; it's so scrawny."

"A thistle smells like a thistle," said Charlotte, "but if you sniff this one, now it will smell like a cedar tree."

"That's right," said Marie. "Let's make it a cedar-thistle tree." She took the branch out of the can and broke it up into little fronds, each one having a few blue berries on it. She arranged them in the thistle so that they looked like little green and blue wisps of decoration. It looked very pretty and the thistle tree smelled just like a cedar tree.

When Clara and Pauline came home for Christmas vacation from Blunt, where they lived in a dormitory during the week while they went to high school, they admired the tree and praised their brother and sisters on the good job they had done decorating it.

The substitute Christmas tree was placed on the organ, and when Ma played *Silent Night*, the tinfoil balls twinkled in the lamplight, and everybody agreed that Marie's idea was a big success.

Ma and Daddy's wedding portrait in 1913

The Ditzler Place

Daddy behind the wheel of his Model T Ford, Ma holding Ted, with Clara, Charlotte, Marie and Pauline

**Ma holding Ted under an elm tree on the Ditzler place,
with Charlotte, Clara, Marie and Pauline (in tree)**

Happy Hollow School

The Uecker children pose with their classmates at Crocus Hill School. Back Row: Evelyn, Vivian and Annabel Hall, Bud Young, Ivan Mc-Millan and Darrell Russell. Middle Row: Agnes Young, Pauline, Rose Cunningham, Thelma Young and Ralph McMillan. Front Row: Marie, Clara, Elaine Hall and Charlotte

The Uecker children and their classmates at recess, Crocus Hill School. On the left, Kathryn McCue, Evelyn Hall, and Rose Cunningham in back; Charlotte and Ted Uecker in front. On the right, Bobbie Cunningham in back; Elaine Hall and Marie in the middle; Rollie Hall in front

Ted in overalls next to Beans on the Congdon Place, with
friends who are probably Alvin and Rollie Hall

Grace Abernathy with Charlotte, Goldie, Ted and Sonny in front

The Uecker family out on the prairie in the early 1940s: Daddy, Ma, Marie, George, Pauline, Ted, Florence, Goldie, Clara, and Charlotte with Sonny in front

Sonny on Buster, in front of the Uecker home near Giddings

Charlotte, Goldie, Sonny (with dog Skippy) and George

Charlotte, Florence, Marie and Goldie by a haystack

Charlotte dressed up for teaching school at Hilltop

Just married: Chas and Charlotte in 1945

Chas and Charlotte's children in the early 1950s: Jerilyn in back, and
Terrill, Dan, Ross and Chuck in front

Hard Times

The drought reduced the springs to trickles and the creek stopped running, leaving only waterholes and the springs' outlets. This in turn caused many of the huge cottonwood and elm trees around the house to die. They were chopped down and used for firewood, probably improving access to the place, but Charlotte would run off and cry every time one was cut down. Those closest to the springs survived, providing shade and protection for the buildings.

A short distance from the house, there was a cellar. The sides, ceiling and steps were cement. The cellar was very cool in the summer and never froze in the winter. The family kept the cream separator down there, and the cream was kept fairly sweet for the once-a-week trip to Harrold. Ma would sour the skim milk to a mild clabber, which all the children loved. This type of milk clabber is now called yogurt. Ma also made lots of cottage cheese, winter and summer. There was generally butter in the summer, but Ma and Daddy were reluctant to use much of the cream to make it, because the cream was needed to buy groceries, food and clothing for the family.

Daddy taught Ted and Charlotte how to set snares and traps, and they caught pheasants and partridges for food. The family could not eat rabbits, though there were lots of them, because they had boils, probably due to malnutrition. One time, when food was very short, the children saw a grouse high up in a tree and went to tell Ma. She had a small rifle, and they were able to find only one shell. She went out and took aim, saying, "you'd better pray this one hits." The children had faith in her, because they knew she was a good shot, and she didn't let them down. They had grouse with homemade noodles for supper that night.

Daddy would manage to buy a small pig somewhere, and after it was fattened with slops from the kitchen and some purchased grain, it would be butchered. That would be the only meat and frying lard for the year.

The 1930s were the years of the Great Depression. It was also a time of drought and dust storms. What little crops and livestock the farmers did raise could not be sold for a decent price. As a result, many of the Ueckers' neighbors, including the McMillans and Halls, had sold what little property they had and were moving West, where there was the promise of work.

One summer night, the McMillans came to visit the family. Mac McMillan, his wife Goldie, and their boys Ivan and Ralph had come to tell them that they were having a sale and would move away the next week. The Ueckers were sorry to see them go. They had been good friends. Mrs. McMillan had kept Goldie and Ted for over two weeks when George was born and Ma was in the hospital in Onida. Goldie loved Mrs. McMillan, who had the same name she did. She called her "Ma Mac."

Ma and Daddy and the two smallest children went to the McMillan sale, leaving Marie, Ted, Goldie and Charlotte to take potato bugs off of a patch of potatoes that Daddy had planted across the creek (Pauline and Clara were staying at their Uncle Ted and Aunt Florence Schenegge's place in the Big Bend of the Missouri River at that time). The main garden was a little ways from the house. Once the children finished with the potato patch, they were to look for bugs in the main garden. Daddy had put kerosene in each of their cans and told them he wanted all of the bugs picked off by the time he returned.

It was a hot day, and it suddenly got very cloudy. The children were relieved that perhaps it would cool off. Then they looked up into the sky and saw that the strange cloudiness was a horde of beetles coming in against the sun. They were huge and black, with another swarm of gray ones coming in after them. The children frantically picked them off the potatoes and put them in the cans, only to have them crawl out again for lack of enough kerosene to kill them. Charlotte and the others then picked up sticks and began to club them, but still, they kept coming in. They were working so hard at it that they never noticed Ma and Daddy had come home until Daddy started taking the sticks away, telling them it was no use, and to go into the house and cool off. By nightfall, the potato patch and garden were stripped clean.

Those were discouraging years. The sale had been a disaster for the McMillans. Once the bugs started swarming in, the neighbors left. Daddy bought a couple of items for a nickel, which was all that he could afford. One of the items was a homemade sled with wide runners, but no steering mechanism. It was the fastest sled in the neighborhood and the children fought over who was going to use it, even though they had another good sled that they could steer.

The years of the Depression were difficult for the Uecker family. There were times when there was very little food in the house. Ma was a good cook and would have to stretch what little there was. Because of this, many times the family went to bed hungry. One family who had moved on the Lamphere Place after they left (a man, his wife, and three little boys) could be counted on to appear over their hill just as Ma was putting supper on the table. Finally, Ma and Pauline and Clara decided to put supper on an hour earlier, so the family would be finished eating when they arrived. When they came, the Uecker girls were doing the dishes, and the oldest boy started to cry. When his mother tried to hush him, he said, "But I'm so hungry!" Daddy told Ma to put some food on the table for them. This paid off to some degree, as the father had mechanical skills and helped keep their old car in repair. He would sometimes manage to come up with enough money for gas to take the cream to Harrold and pick up the mail. He and Daddy also sawed wood together, and he would help split the larger logs. Wood for the cook stove was Charlotte's job, and she became very handy with the bucksaw and axe, later graduating to help Daddy with the crosscut saw on the big trees.

After their youngest child died from pneumonia, the family moved to Idaho. Jack and Frank Garrigan then built a small home into a side hill on the Lamphere Place and moved their cattle over there, except for the ones the Ueckers were milking. Those milk cows were the difference between the family eating and starvation.

They were not able to raise garden vegetables because of the drought and insects. So, they ate only what they could buy with the cream check. John Bohning, at Bohning's Store in Harrold, permitted the family to charge groceries when they did not have any money. His generosity paid off when prosperity returned. Most of his customers repaid him in full and remained faithful as long as Bohnings owned the Store, which was until Jack Bohning, his son, retired many years later.

By the mid-1930s, the Uecker family began receiving federal food assistance, which included staples such as rice and beans, as well as oranges and grapefruit from time to time. This provided the children with citrus and made it a little easier to get by. There were also two new babies, Florence and Sonny, making nine children who had to be fed and clothed. Clara and Pauline often worked for Uncle Ted, Ma's youngest brother, and Aunt Florence, his wife, and she would pay them by making them clothes. Uncle Ted and Aunt Florence helped the Ueckers all they could, but times were tough for everybody. When Charlotte was twelve, she stayed with a neighbor and her children for a few days so the neighbor would have someone in the house when she went to the barn to milk and care for the horses. They paid her twenty-five cents, and she gave it to Ma and Daddy to buy groceries.

John Gerlt, the neighbor over the hill, was a bachelor and a good farmer. He always hired one of the Uecker children if he had a small job to do, and he always paid well. He had lots of chickens, and he didn't charge Ma as much for eggs as he received for them in town. He would also put in a few extra eggs every time Ma bought them. He liked the Uecker kids, because Ma and Daddy did not allow them to go over unless they were invited or had been sent to his house on an errand. The children were not allowed to use a slingshot to shoot birds because John liked them, and he always fed the pheasants and grouse along with his chickens. He also liked animals and treated his own like they were best friends. Charlotte loved animals, too, and sometimes would manage to find her way over when she was looking for pigs or turkeys, even though she knew they weren't there. He always talked to her like she was another grownup, sometimes giving her an apple so there wouldn't be any evidence when she got home, because he knew she didn't have permission to be there. Once when Charlotte was practicing trick riding on Buster, he was out looking for pigs and saw her. He told her he was going to tell Daddy that he had quite a trick rider in the family. Charlotte practically got on her knees to beg him not to tell. He promised he wouldn't, and he never did. He later married Marian Mathews. She was one of Charlotte's favorite neighbors from the time she had stayed with her family when George was born, and she was pleased that her two favorite people were married to each other.

The Sled

When Ma and Daddy went to the McMillans' sale, they bought a pile of junk for ten cents. Daddy had decided that some of it could be used for repairing some of his own horse-drawn machinery, but the main reason he bought it was that he saw an old homemade sled near the bottom of the pile.

Daddy examined the sled after he and Ma arrived home and looked through the pile of junk. He found it to be in very good condition. It didn't have a steering device in front to guide it, but it had homemade steel runners, good cross pieces and a strong, wide board on top to sit or lie on. A two-by-four was nailed on the front, but there were no holes in it for attaching a pulling rope. Daddy got out his brace and bit and drilled a hole into each side of the two-by-four, put a small rope through one hole, and tied a knot in the end. Then he measured the length to just the right size to pull a sled, cut it off, put the end through the other hole and tied a knot in it. "There," he said, "when we get some snow, there will be two sleds and, I hope, not so much fighting over who gets to slide downhill."

The Uecker children weren't very impressed with the new sled. They liked the one their uncles and aunts had given them for Christmas several years before. They could steer it past the rocks when they slid down hill, and it could hold at least three of them. The sled Daddy bought at the sale would barely hold two.

The little home on Chapelle Creek was an ideal place for sledding. It was protected from the strong winds by hills and trees, and there were many hills that were just right to glide down. There was even a short, steep hill near the house that was great fun for the small children. The older children would ride down it on a scoop shovel, or on home-made skis made from barrel staves. There was another steep hill by the spring that was dangerous when covered with ice, and Ma didn't like to see the older children slide down it, though it was great fun. If they turned just at the right time when they reached the bottom, they could go for a long distance up the creek. It they didn't make the turn at the right time, the sled would go up the steep creek bank opposite the hill, dumping everybody off in a flurry of snow, screams, and laughter. This was the hill that all the children in the neighborhood loved, and a great many hours were spent sliding down the ice-covered slope with everyone trying to keep from being thrown off their sleds on the steep bank beyond.

When winter came and the snow fell on the hills, Clara, Pauline and Marie claimed the long sled that could be steered for their own, and the short homemade sled was given to Charlotte, Ted and Goldie. Charlotte was angry. She thought they could at least take turns, and she, Ted and Goldie grumpily took off for a hill in the opposite direction from the older girls. Ma told them to be careful because they couldn't steer it, and she didn't want them to run into any rocks and hurt themselves.

"It probably won't even get as far as a rock," Charlotte complained, as she sat down on the sled to give it the first try and to break a trail for the smaller children. Ted gave her a shove and she was surprised to see how it shot forward, skimming over the snow with Charlotte shrieking as it picked up speed. It veered towards a big rock, and Charlotte rolled off just in time while the sled shot to the bottom of the hill. Charlotte ran after it and pulled it back to where Ted and Goldie stood excitedly at the top of the hill. "Whew," she puffed, "that was a fast ride! Maybe we got the best deal after all. If I could only steer it, it would be the best sled I ever rode on." Then she picked out a place where there weren't any rocks, and they had great fun sliding downhill all morning long.

"That little sled is a good sled, Daddy," said Ted at lunchtime. "But we can't steer it."

"It's good enough for you," said one of the older girls. "You shouldn't go down the steep hills anyway." The older girls were afraid Daddy would worry if the younger ones couldn't guide the sled and make them take the homemade one. He knew they would be able to roll off if they came to a rock or a steep bank.

That afternoon Daddy climbed the hill where the smaller children were sliding. "I bought that pile of junk because I saw that sled," he explained. "It looks just like a wide runner homemade sled I had when I was a boy. We guided it by leaning one way or another. Here, I'll show you." Daddy adjusted his big frame on the sled, nearly covering it up, and Charlotte gave him a shove. Down the hill he went like an arrow, his weight making the snow fly. But Daddy was heading straight into a big rock!

"Watch him pile off!" shouted Ted, but instead Daddy leaned way over towards the rock and the little sled shot the other way so fast it turned over, spilling Daddy into the snow. Daddy brought the sled back to the top of the hill. "That's how it is done," he said. "Only you'll have to get used to it. It won't dump you if you lean just right." The children soon found that the little sled was almost too fast for the spring hill, and it was a long time before they could slide down the ice-covered hill, then turn to go down the creek. The sled would have them dumped into the opposite bank almost before they could think, but they learned how to maneuver it before winter was over.

"It's my very favorite sled," said Charlotte as she put it up in the haymow when the snow thawed and melted away the next spring. "I'm going to hang it up here so nothing will happen to it." And she took good care of that little sled, until she grew up and left home to go to high school.

The Water Pail

The Uecker house, like most homes at the time, did not have indoor plumbing. The family had to keep the big water pail that stood on the washstand filled with water. It was used for drinking, cooking and washing their hands and faces, and with a large family like the Ueckers, it never took long for it to disappear.

The water bucket had a tin dipper in it, and the washbasin sat beside it on the washstand. Beside the basin was a soap dish that held a bar of Ma's homemade lye soap. When there was enough money from the cream check, a bar of castile soap replaced the lye soap. Lye soap was good for washing clothes, but when it was used for washing faces and hands, it would make their skin raw and red. The washstand stood between the door and the east window. A towel hung from a nail beside the window.

Marie, Charlotte and Ted usually carried the water for the house. They carried gallon syrup pails to the well by the creek, pumped them full of cold spring water and carried them up the hill. They would pour them into the bucket on the stand and then make another trip to the well. It took two trips to fill the bucket, and they made the trip several times a day. After school started, they had to fill the bucket before they went to school and keep it filled when they got home. They decided among themselves to take turns, so each one would not have to worry about keeping the water bucket filled for two days. When it was their turn, Ma kept them busy running back and forth to the well during the day and they had to see that the bucket was full every night, so there would be water for her to get breakfast and for everyone to wash their hands and faces when they got up in the morning.

The house stood on a knoll above the creek. The path below the knoll wound through a thicket of chokecherry and plum trees, and just beyond that were four big cottonwood trees that stood on the creek bank. The well, fed from a spring, was dug near the biggest tree and the water was delicious and cold. It was a long way from the house, and the big water pails were too heavy for the children to carry, so Ma kept gallon syrup pails ready for them to fill. They would carry one in each hand through the thickets and up the little hill to the house where she would take them and pour them into the big water pail, then set them beside the door for them to take on the next trip.

The children didn't mind the trips to the well during the day. They liked to watch the chickens dusting themselves in the ash pile beside the path, as well as the goldfinches, wrens and wild canaries that hopped and sang in the chokecherry trees. When the chokecherries were ripe, a small handful of the purple berries tasted good, even if they were mostly pits. The tall cottonwood trees reached high into the sky. Catbirds, kingfishers, woodpeckers, thrushes and flickers could be seen flying from tree to tree all day long. The killdeers ran along the creek bank, chirping *killdeer, killdeer* as they ran limping and falling, pretending they had a broken wing to lure the children's attention away from the nests so they wouldn't find them. In the evening, the nighthawks would swoop and make harsh cries as they came up from their dive during their chase for insects. Most interesting of all was the swinging nest in the cottonwood tree next to the well. A pair of Baltimore orioles nested there every year, and sometimes the children would forget about carrying water while they watched them feed their baby birds in the nest that swung gently to and fro in the summer breeze.

Though the children enjoyed going to the well during the day, the trips after dark were another matter. The distance seemed much longer when it was night, and the sounds were different. Instead of the happy daytime sounds, owls would cry out a mournful *who who-oo*, twigs would snap, and the hens would occasionally squawk in the chicken house. The horses would snort, while the cows would stop and swish their tails. Sometimes a rustling could be heard in the plum thicket and a coyote would howl from the top of the big hill in John Gerlt's pasture.

Marie and Ted did not like to go to the well when night came, but Charlotte didn't mind. She liked to be outdoors and spent as much time as she could on the creek. She had grown to understand what the sounds were, and the coyotes didn't frighten her. Daddy had told her they were scared of humans, and she believed him. Didn't they slink away whenever they saw someone in the daytime? She was sure they would do it at night as well. When they first moved to the creek their howling at the moon frightened her, but she had grown accustomed to it, and if it did seem a little scary, she had their dog Beans by her side and knew nothing would bother her when he was with her.

The night sounds scared Marie and Ted, yet whenever it was their turn to fill the water pails, they would play too long and it would be dark before they realized they hadn't filled the water bucket on the washstand. Ma usually reminded them in time, but when she was very busy she would forget, because it didn't make any difference whether it was light or dark when it was Charlotte's turn. Since they were so frightened, she would tell Charlotte to go with them.

One Saturday in late fall, Charlotte and Daddy worked all day long sawing and chopping wood for the cook stove. Ma had reminded Marie to fill the water bucket when it was still daylight, but Marie was playing with the smaller children and decided to wait. She was sure Ma would make Charlotte go with her. Whenever it was dark, Ma would automatically tell Charlotte to go along with whoever had the turn, and Charlotte would always help carry the water. Nobody ever went along with Charlotte, though, to help carry the pails when it was her turn.

Charlotte was very tired when Ma told her to help Marie, and she asked if they could carry it in the morning. Ma very sharply refused. There wasn't time for her or Daddy to carry it in the morning, and it would be too difficult to get Marie up earlier to carry the water. Charlotte grumbled while she put her outdoor clothes on, and Ma scolded her for being so cranky. Daddy looked at Ma after they left the house and asked, "Do they do that all the time?"

"Just about," Ma confessed, "but Charlotte isn't scared, and they refuse to go unless she goes along, so what can I do? Sometimes it is my fault when I forget, but usually I tell them when it is still daylight."

The next day, Charlotte and Daddy sawed and chopped the smaller branches of the tree they had cut down the day before. With Ted and Marie's help, they stacked the wood so it would be easy to carry in when winter came. Charlotte had been helping since early morning, and she was very tired by the end of the day.

It was Ted's turn to fill the water pail. He always waited until the last minute to do his chores. He was a happy little boy and played so well with the other children, that he would forget when it was his turn to fill the water bucket until it was too late. He called to Charlotte to come along, and Charlotte got up from studying her lessons and went to put her jacket on.

Daddy had just carried another armful of wood into the house. He looked at Charlotte and said, "Go back to your book. Marie can go with him tonight."

Marie turned pale, and Ma started to remonstrate.

"No," said Daddy. "If they can't remember, they will have to go together until they get so they can remember. There is nothing to be afraid of anyway."

Ted and Marie put their coats on, gathered up the water pails and went fearfully out into the night. Charlotte was worried. She knew they really were afraid of the dark and she offered to go along, but Daddy said "No" in a tone that Charlotte knew meant no argument, so she sat down with her book.

Soon Ted and Marie dashed in with only a half pail of water slopping over the edge, slamming the door wildly behind them. "What's wrong?" exclaimed Ma.

"There was a big noise!" cried Ted. "And it was right behind us! I know something followed us right up to the house!"

Charlotte went to the door and opened it. She heard a *who, who-oo* coming from the trees down beside the creek. She closed the door. "It's only a hoot owl," she said. "I'd better go back with them."

Daddy went outside and looked around. He came back in and said to Ted and Marie, "Go back and fill your pails with water. Take the dog with you. I want you to come back slowly and when you come through the door, I want you to shut it very carefully." He went to the rocking chair by the heating stove and sat down. He sat George and Florence on his knee and started rocking them to sleep while Goldie stood on one of the rockers and, leaning over the arm of the chair, told him stories about what she'd done all day.

Ted and Marie opened the door. They came in carefully and closed it behind them. Their water pails were full and Ma emptied them into the big pail on the washstand. They took off their jackets and sat down to do their homework without saying a word.

"What did you think you heard?" Charlotte whispered to Marie after they had gone to bed.

"It sounded awful, but when we really listened, we only heard old Brindle down in the creek," Marie answered. "She was stomping in the water."

"You've heard that hundreds of times," said Charlotte. "You should have known what that sound was."

"I know," said Marie, "but it sounds different and scarier at night."

Ted and Marie remembered most of the time after that to carry the water during daylight when it was their turn. If they did forget and Charlotte didn't go along, they would go together and were not so afraid. They had learned to take their time, and understand what the night sounds were. Above all, like Charlotte, they would take Beans along just in case a skunk decided to cross their path. A growl from Beans meant there was something unusual nearby, and they would run to the house to tell Ma and Daddy.

The Blizzard

"I don't think I'll send the younger ones to school today," announced Ma. "It is too cold, and the wind might come up. A January blizzard can be real bad."

"Maybe we should stay home, too," said Marie. "It blows a lot worse on the hill."

"I think we'd better go," said Charlotte, starting to pull on her heavy, black sweater. "We should be studying for our six weeks' tests, and we'd better go every day we can."

"You are right," agreed Marie, and she started after her coat and cap.

"Put some extra stockings on and be sure to wear your scarves," Ma said. "I'll get your lunch ready while you get your wraps on."

The two girls dressed warmly. They still wore the nice wool stocking caps that Aunt Elsie in the far-off state of Washington had sent them for Christmas before they started to school. Now they were both in the eighth grade, and they wrapped the scarves that matched the caps tightly around their collars. Ma tied them in the back, leaving enough room in the last wrap so they could pull it up over their faces if the air was too cold.

Charlotte and Marie started down the little hill to the lane that led to the road that went up the long hill toward the schoolhouse. Their breath steamed high into the cold air, frosting their caps and eyebrows. "It really is cold," said Marie. "Yes-s," shivered Charlotte. "And I've got so many clothes on, I can hardly walk. I thought Ma was going to bring Daddy's big coat out next." "Maybe she would have," giggled Marie, "if there had been two of them." Then they quit talking and started walking briskly up the long hill.

Ma had stepped outside to see what the weather was like and she saw some high swirls of snow rising on top of the hill. She decided it was too cold for the girls to face into the raw northwest wind. She called to them to come back, but their ears were wrapped tightly into their coat collars and scarves and they could not hear her. She put on her coat and ran to the barn to find Daddy, thinking perhaps his voice could reach them, but he was not there. He was across the creek at the big thistle stack, feeding the milk cows. Ma did not like to leave the small children home alone very long with the hot stoves that were keeping the house warm, so she ran back to the house, hoping the girls would decide to turn around and come back. Daddy would soon be back from feeding the cows, and she would tell him then.

When Charlotte and Marie reached the top of the hill, a gust of wind hit them and nearly knocked them down. "Maybe we should go back," said Charlotte, pulling her scarf up over her face. Marie had already covered hers before they reached the top.

"No," answered Marie. "It isn't very far across the pasture, and I can see the schoolhouse. We are over halfway there, so we might as well go on."

They took each other's hands and, bending into the wind that hit them sideways from the northwest, hastened toward the fence that bordered John Gerlt's pasture. Then Charlotte parted the wires and Marie crawled through, carrying the dinner pail. Charlotte followed, taking her by the arm, but this time she walked on the west side so the wind would hit her first, protecting Marie, who got cold easily. They struggled on, and all at once the schoolhouse disappeared behind a cloud of swirling snow caused by the wind cutting into the drifts, loosening more and more snow and swirling it higher into the air until they could no longer see the schoolhouse.

"It's a ground blizzard," gasped Charlotte. "We've got to hurry. Just keep walking straight ahead, and we'll hit the schoolyard fence." They struggled on, the wind grabbing at their clothes and blowing away the lid of the lard pail that held their lunch. Charlotte started to chase it, but Marie said, "Let it go. Let's just get to the schoolhouse." Charlotte decided she was right, even though Ma always seemed to have a hard time finding lids to fit their lunch pails, so she grabbed Marie's arm again.

They walked silently, trying to keep a foothold in the blowing snow, and then Marie shouted above the wind, "We're going the wrong way! Let's go this way," and she turned southwest, directly toward the open pasture. Charlotte turned, then realized that the wind was no longer hitting her face from the same direction.

"No!" she cried. "Turn around. It's this way!" Marie started to argue, flailing her arms at Charlotte, but Charlotte held her firmly by the elbow and started again towards what she hoped was the fence that surrounded the schoolyard. *I'm glad it's a big schoolyard*, she thought grimly as they struggled into the white wall of swirling snow. *If I touch just one post, I'll know where I am.* Marie walked slower and slower, then dropped the lunch pail. "I'm cold," she whimpered. "I can't feel my feet." Charlotte grabbed the lunch pail. "Stomp your feet," she cried, "and keep going. We know it isn't far, and we'll freeze to death if we don't keep moving!"

"You've got us lost," gasped Marie. "I just know we are going in the wrong direction!" Just then, they bumped up against the corner post on the southwest side of the schoolyard. *Whew!* thought Charlotte. *We just made it. Another few feet, and we would have gone right past the schoolyard and out into the pasture.* She turned, still pulling Marie by the arm, following the wire with her hand until she got to where the wire was loose by the crooked post with a jagged forked top. She pulled Marie through the fence. She still could not see the schoolhouse, even though it was only a short distance away, but she knew that if they walked in a straight line they would come up against the step, so she shut everything off in her mind except just the thought of the schoolhouse by walking straight ahead. She knew Marie would not be able to go much further as she had fallen into the snow and refused to get up. Charlotte grabbed her by the arm. "Get up!" she demanded. "You'll freeze to death. You know that."

"I can't," sobbed Marie. "My feet won't move." Charlotte thought about leaving her and getting to the schoolhouse to get Miss Loughlin to help her, but she was afraid she might miss it and would have to try again, and Marie, who still thought they were lost, might try to struggle off in another direction. It was no use calling. The entrance hall was in the front of the schoolhouse, and the door to the schoolroom was always tightly closed in cold weather. Miss Loughlin, who lived in the schoolroom, would never hear her the way the wind was screaming. She reached down and grabbed Marie again by the right arm. Her sister fought her, saying her arm hurt, so Charlotte wrapped her arms around her and dragged her backward, struggling against the wind and snow. Her eyes were streaming, her feet were numb and her chest hurt, but she knew that if she was right in her aim towards the front step, they had just a few yards to go. She had dragged Marie only a few feet when the schoolhouse loomed like a huge shadow right in front of them. "I see it!" she shouted, but Marie didn't answer. She heard Charlotte dully, but she was too exhausted to respond. But Charlotte didn't know that. *She's frozen to death*, she thought. *What will Ma and Daddy say? It's all my fault. I was the one who thought we should go to school.* She lifted Marie up on the step and started to open the door.

Miss Loughlin heard the thud on the step. She rushed to the door. She had not expected any pupils because of the storm. She opened the door to find a very cold, snow-covered Charlotte with a lunch pail frozen to her mitten, pulling Marie over the porch. She pushed Charlotte into the hall and picked Marie up, carrying her into the schoolhouse.

"Is she dead?" quavered Charlotte. "No," said Miss Loughlin as she pulled off Marie's snow-caked wraps. "Get your wraps off, and what are you doing with that pail?" Charlotte had tried to pull the pail out of her mitten before she started dragging Marie, but it was stuck tight. She looked down. "Why, it's empty," she said, surprised. "What will we eat for lunch?"

"I have food," said Miss Loughlin. "Just get your wraps off and stay away from the stove. Get over there by the window and start jumping up and down to thaw your feet." Marie, who until now had been quiet, regained her breath and was sobbing because her feet were numb.

Miss Loughlin rushed out and filled the wash pan with snow. She pulled Marie's stockings off, pushed up her long underwear and started patting the snow gently on her feet. Marie cried out when she felt the snow. "They aren't frozen, thank heaven," said Miss Loughlin. "She wouldn't feel the snow if they were." She put the pan of snow aside and poured some hot water from the pan that always sat on the stove into two other pans. Then she added snow until the water was slightly warm. "Both of you put your feet in this water and soon, they will feel better," she told them. She took their stockings and outer clothes and draped them over the warm stove jacket to dry. "I have a feeling your Dad will be here soon," she said. "Why didn't you turn around when you saw there was a blizzard?"

"I thought we could make it," said Marie. "The biggest distance from home is to the top of the hill, and we were well over halfway here."

"Let this be a lesson to you," scolded Miss Loughlin. "Next time you see a ground blizzard on the hill, turn around and go home. I grew up on the river bottom. The schoolhouse was just on top of the hill, and my sisters and I nearly got lost in a ground blizzard when we reached the top and the schoolhouse was almost in front of us. We could see the top of it when we climbed the hill, then the wind blew the snow higher than our heads and we couldn't see it at all. We went back down the hill a little ways until we could see the top of it again, then aimed directly for it, and we got there safe and sound. Ground blizzards are just as dangerous as other blizzards when the snow is falling, and I want you to promise me you won't ever try walking in one again."

"We won't," they promised in chorus.

The stockings and mittens were still steaming on the stove jacket when the door flew open and Daddy rushed in. He had hitched the team up immediately after Ma had told him the girls had walked over the hill. He had torn down the pasture fence and driven through, staying right on their path. He was worried they had, like so many people do in a swirling blizzard, become mixed up in their directions and were lying out on the prairie. He tied the team to the schoolyard fence and hurried into the schoolhouse just on the chance they might have found their way.

Daddy gathered the girls into his arms. "Thank God," he said. "How in the world did you get here? I was sure you were lost!"

"Charlotte dragged me in," Marie said proudly. "I kept wanting to go another direction and she wouldn't let me, but we lost the lid to the dinner pail, and also the lunch." Daddy and Miss Loughlin looked at each other and laughed.

"What are you laughing about?" asked Charlotte, still remembering how scared she was when she thought Marie was frozen to death. "It wasn't funny."

"We know that," consoled Miss Loughlin, "but when people get real frightened or upset, sometimes they laugh or cry, so we laughed. It made your Dad and me feel better."

"Oh," said Charlotte. When she thought about it, she realized she did the same thing herself, but she didn't know that grownups felt that way, too. She could understand them better now, she thought.

"Just how did you know you were going in the right direction?" asked Miss Loughlin, as Daddy warmed himself by the stove while she helped them get ready to go back home with him.

"I remembered Daddy talking about that year he was in Canada when he went trapping animals up there," Charlotte answered. "He said the wind didn't blow much, but when it did, it was terrible, and my uncle who had trapped there a long time told him always to remember which side the wind hit him and to always walk with that in mind. That way, he would always be moving in the general direction of wherever he wanted to go. So, I did just that. Marie turned me around so that the wind was nearly at our backs, and I was sure we were going southeast. I suppose we would have hit the pasture fence again, but it would have taken me too long to find out where we were, so I just made her come along in what I thought was the right direction with the wind hitting me on the left side of my face. I was sure hoping I was right," she added, "and I almost did miss the schoolyard even then."

"What you did was exactly right," said Daddy, fondly squeezing her shoulder. "Now let's go get in the wagon and go home. Ma is worried nearly to death, and I'm sure she'll have something hot for us to drink when we get there."

Once Charlotte and Marie got their coats and wraps back on, he picked them up, one in each arm. Miss Loughlin opened the door and Daddy carried them out, put them deep down into the wagon and piled some hay loosely over them. "Giddap!" he said after he had untied Rosie and Bob and had climbed into the wagon. The team turned around and they were headed home with the blizzard still screaming wildly around them. "Maybe they'll get lost, too," said Marie fearfully.

"I was worried about finding the schoolyard when I was driving them here," confessed Daddy as he tied the reins around the standard and settled down beside them, "because I was driving them away from home, but I did just what Charlotte did. I remembered where the wind was coming from. But going home," he explained, "you don't interfere. This team knows the way. You'll see."

Soon they were going down the long hill and all at once the screaming of the wind stopped, and everything was different. "I can see!" exclaimed Marie. "It's snowy, but I can see everywhere," said Charlotte.

"That's right," answered Daddy. "The hills cut off the wind and you don't notice the weather so much down here. If I had seen you leave the house, I would have made you go back because I could tell the wind was starting to blow big clouds of snow on top of the hills, but it's all right. You are safe, and that's all that matters." By that time, they were in front of the house and Daddy lifted them out of the wagon into a tearful Ma's arms.

BUSTER

"Come and see the new horses," said Ma to Ted. "Two of them are tame enough for you smaller ones to ride. Jack and Frank will ride the other one until he is ready." Jack and Frank Garrigan were their neighbors, and they and Daddy often helped each other with the farm work.

Ted sat up in bed and rubbed his eyes. "Let's get Charlotte up right now. We want to see the horses before breakfast."

"Where did they come from?" Charlotte asked unbelievingly when Ma woke her up.

"Daddy traded the working mare's colts for them," answered Ma. "Frank and Jack took the colts to their new owner yesterday and brought the new horses back late last night. It was a long trip," she went on. "They had to lead the work colts all the way, then lead the horses Daddy traded them for back here. I fed them a real late supper and when they get up, they will help you with the horses."

Charlotte and Ted dressed quickly and ran out to the corral. There stood four horses, a blue roan part-Morgan horse, a small gray mustang, a big white horse and a small white part-mustang pony. Daddy came up to the corral. "The gray one is called Buster," he said. "The big white one's name is Tom, and the smaller one is Billy. Billy swings his front foot a little when he runs, but he is a good little pony and I think he'll be a nice horse for you to ride. Jack wants to buy the blue roan horse tied in the corner. He has already named him Smoky."

Pauline, Clara and Marie came running up to the corral. "The gray one is mine," Pauline announced. "The rest of the kids can have the other two."

"I don't know about that," Daddy answered. "I thought when Buster got broke a little better, you could all share."

By that time, Frank and Jack had eaten their breakfast. They came out to the corral and put the children on the horses while they led them around the corral.

Tom was the gentlest of the horses. Ted and Charlotte rode him all over. Someone had to help them mount, but after they were on his broad back, they rode him back and forth in the corral. Once he thought it was safe enough, Daddy put Goldie and George on in front of Charlotte, and they would ride happily around the little clearing in front of the barn. One day, Pauline put little George on by himself. Tom grazed under a cottonwood tree and a branch scraped George off onto the ground. George cried a little and then wanted back on, so Daddy lifted him up and put one of the other children on behind him. He told them George was too little to ride by himself, so they either had to ride with him or lead the horse while he was on him.

When Daddy thought Marie, Charlotte and Ted could ride well enough, he caught Billy and put him in the corral so they could ride him when they wanted to. Billy was fun. He went faster than Tom, and he was easier to climb onto. They rode their horses bareback, and they loved Billie's gait even though he swung his front leg out when he galloped.

Times were hard, and money was scarce in the thirties. One day, Daddy came in and said he had to sell two of the horses. He had a good offer for Buster, and he was going to sell him and one of the other ones. He decided to keep Billy. He was a good little horse and tame enough for all of the children to ride.

Pauline and Clara didn't want to sell Buster, because he was a fast little horse and they liked him best.

"Can't we keep him?" they asked. "We'll take good care of him and break him for all of us to ride."

"Well, I am a little worried about Billie's limp," said

Daddy. "I'll sell him and Tom, but all the children will own Buster. He is going to be a good pony."

Ted was sad when the neighbor came to get Billie and Tom. He especially liked Billie, and he had tears in his eyes when the neighbor led them over the hill. "I wish we could have kept him," he said. "He was such a nice little horse."

Ma knelt down beside him. "We wish we didn't have to sell him, Ted, but we need the money. You'll soon be able to ride Buster, and perhaps we can get another horse for you later on."

Pauline wasn't happy about sharing Buster with the younger children. She would think up excuses so no one but she or Clara would ride him. One day when she was riding, Buster shied at a rabbit that bounded up from a grass clump. His quick jump threw her to the ground, and she insisted he wasn't safe for the smaller children. "You are the one who fell off, Pauline," Ted reminded her. "We haven't fallen off him yet."

Buster was a clever little horse, and always managed to run away whenever someone wanted to ride him. Daddy had fenced in a small pasture east of the barn, so he could graze and could be caught if he or one of the older girls had to ride him. The creek ran through the lot and big trees grew on either side. The west end of the pasture was covered with trees and a huge cottonwood stood in the corner by the gate. Ted, Marie, Charlotte and Goldie would clasp their hands with each other to see if they could reach around it but no matter how hard they tried, they couldn't touch hands all around. Sometimes Clara would join in the fun and grasp hands with them, so they could all reach around the tree.

There was a diamond willow tree in the pasture. In the early fall, it would be covered with orange and black monarch butterflies. The children would stand still with their hands outspread and the butterflies would alight all over them.

The fence that separated John Gerlt's pasture from the Uecker Place was on the north side of the lot. It rose to the top of the hill. On top of the hill were three rings of stones. Daddy said they were tepee rings and that Indians a long time ago lived on top of the hills, where they could catch the breeze while they were hunting for buffalo, digging the wild turnips and onions that grew on the hills, or gathering wild chokecherries and plums from the creek bottom to dry for the winter.

To the east of the creek was a gully, and on the south side of that rose another high hill. Wild crocuses grew on that hill. Ted, Marie and Charlotte loved to pick the pretty lavender flowers in the early spring to take to Ma or to the teacher when they went to school. The fence on the east side was on the other side of the hill and formed the outer boundary of the Uecker farm. There was a field on top of the hill that stretched to the south. On the south and west side of the field was the big cow pasture. Just on top of the hill on the south side of the gully, another fence came down going through the creek and up past the cottonwood tree toward the barn corral. That marked the south side of the lot where Buster was kept.

The lot was a pretty place near the creek with lots of flowers. Tiny minnows flashed in the water as it rippled down under the lot fence and into the fenced cow lot that enclosed the spring. Chapelle Creek ran around the barn and house on the north and east sides, over the crossing to the south side of the farm, through another of John Gerlt's pastures and on down through neighboring pastures, ending at DeGrey where it flowed into the Missouri River.

"It's funny," said Ted to Charlotte. "When it's Pauline and Clara's turn to go after the milk cows, they take Buster. When it's Marie's or yours or my turn, we have to walk, and it's a long way. I know I can ride Buster. Daddy put me on him, and I rode him all over the corral."

"I know I can, too," answered Charlotte. "I caught him in the lot and rode him all over without a halter.

I did that with the work colts too, before Daddy sold them, and one of them was always jumping around."

Charlotte always had to gather firewood for the kitchen stove. Because Pauline and Clara helped Ma and Daddy milk cows and run the cream separator, they didn't have to carry wood, feed calves or wash dishes. Those jobs were for the younger children.

One day, while Charlotte was pulling wood out of a trash pile in the creek, she noticed a big stand of sweet clover growing on an open piece of land below the creek bank. She had noticed that Buster had all the sweet clover eaten from his lot, so she broke off an armful and carried it to the fence where Buster was standing, switching flies with his long tail. He quickly ate it and looked at her for more, but Charlotte had to take the wood to the house to chop it into small pieces so Ma could put it in the kitchen range to cook supper. "Goodbye, Buster," she said. "I'll bring you some more tomorrow."

"Buster likes sweet clover," Charlotte said when she sat down to the supper table. "I picked some for him and he ate every bit of it."

"That little pasture is getting short on grass," said Daddy. "I think it's a good idea to take him sweet clover if you can find it. You could take him to the creek bank to graze, Pauline," he went on. "He will get thin if you don't."

Pauline took Buster out to graze for a few days until one morning, Kathryn McCue came over from the John Gerlt Place where she and her parents lived and announced she was starting a club. Rose and Bobbie Cunningham, Jeanne Steiner, Dorothy Meyer, and the Uecker children would be the members.

"I don't know," said Ma. "I need help with the smaller children. We have a garden to weed, and if I do it someone has to watch the little ones."

"Charlotte and Marie can watch them," announced Pauline. "I did it when I was their age."

"Oh, I want them to belong, too," said Kathryn. Marie, Rose and Kathryn, Jeanne and Dorothy were the same age, and Charlotte was two years younger. Bobbie was younger than Charlotte, and Bobbie and Charlotte were best friends.

Ma was not convinced. "The other children do pitch in, but they are too small to weed and help me wash clothes. You and Clara are bigger, and I really do need the help."

That night, Pauline met Daddy as he came home from work and told him that she and Clara would like to belong to the club, as they never got to go anywhere. Marie and Charlotte were big enough to stay with the little ones, and it was time they learned how to weed the garden. She and Clara would be sure to help with washing clothes.

Daddy talked to Ma about it. Ma told Daddy that Kathryn was an only child and she needed someone to play with. Charlotte and Marie would have to stay home to help with Ted, Goldie, George and baby Florence.

Daddy wasn't convinced, but after a steady stream of begging from Pauline and Clara, he finally relented and told them they could belong to the club.

Pauline forgot all about taking Buster out to graze after they had their club. As soon as he heard Charlotte pulling out firewood down on the creek, he would run to the fence waiting for the big armful of sweet clover she always picked for him before she went back to the house. One day, she saw a pile of wood near the creek in Buster's lot. She went to get it and Buster ran up and stopped in front of her, nuzzling her on the shoulder. She was surprised. Buster always ran away when someone wanted to catch him to ride, and it was a chore to get him stopped long enough to halter him. He was hard to catch, and that was why Pauline did not like to take him to graze. When they had oats, it was easy, but they had run out of oats for the horses long ago.

Charlotte petted him for a long time, and he stood nuzzling her hand. Then Charlotte put her hand in his long mane, and he never snorted or jumped. She put her toe just above his knee and swung up on his back, just like she had learned to do with Tom and Billy. He turned his head and looked at her, so she gave him a nudge with her knees and he walked up the creek. *This is fun*, she thought. *I miss Tom and Billy, and I'm going to do this every day when I feed him sweet clover.*

So, every day, Charlotte rode Buster after she fed him an armful of sweet clover. She learned that when she pressed his side with a knee he would turn, so she guided him all over the lot with her hand in his mane. She was afraid he might jump aside if he saw something strange, and she didn't want to fall off.

One afternoon, a cat jumped from a trash pile on the creek and Buster, who was trotting along with Charlotte on his back, jumped aside. Charlotte gasped. *Here I go*, she thought, but she didn't. She had stayed in rhythm with his trotting and when he jumped, she was with him. "I can do it," she whispered. "I don't have to worry about falling off any more."

Not long after that, Daddy told the family he was taking them to Harrold to a small circus. Mr. Bohning, the grocer, had given him tickets for the family, so Ma got George and Florence bathed and put clean clothes on them. Then, she hesitated. "I'd better stay home with the little ones," she told Daddy. "They don't have any shoes. I think you should take Pauline and Clara, though. They are the only ones who have shoes and stockings."

"Oh, get them ready," said Daddy. "It's just a little circus for kids, so they don't have to dress up. And you need to get out, too." The older children ran to wash their faces, hands and feet. They put on clean clothes, Daddy put the can of cream to be sold at Bohning's Cream Station into the trunk, and the family crowded into the car.

The circus was fun. There weren't any wild animals, but there was a magician and a trapeze artist. Charlotte was entranced by a young girl who rode a small pony around the ring. When the horse broke into a trot, the girl stood up on the horse, put her toe in a loop on the strap that was around his belly, and rode around with her other foot in the air. As he went around the ring, she grabbed his mane and slid down his side, riding him around the ring with her long hair trailing on the ground.

The next day, Charlotte tried to stand on Buster's back. He took a step, and she crouched down and took his mane. Before long she could stand on him as he walked along the creek bank, grazing in the short clumps of grass. *I wish I had the halter*, she thought. *I'll bet I could ride him standing on his back when he is trotting.*

One day, when she was carrying wood out of the lot, she felt something cold against her leg. She looked down and saw a big bull snake coil around her leg. She screamed, dropped the firewood and fled to the house, crying for Ma.

Ma was frightened. She looked over her leg for bites. Charlotte was too frightened to remember what kind of snake it was, but she wasn't bitten. She just had a cold feeling on her leg where the snake had wound around it, and she kept crying and rubbing it with her hand to make it go away. Ma put a cloth in some warm water and put it on her leg. When it felt better, Charlotte told her that she had found a big pile of stove wood at the place where the snake wrapped around her leg. Ma asked her if she felt good enough to find it, and she nodded her head tearfully. When she felt better, Ma sent Pauline and Clara to go with her to get the firewood that she had dropped, and to get the wood she had piled up to bring in the next day. Buster ran up to the fence when he saw Charlotte, but as soon as he saw Clara and Pauline following behind, he ran into the woods.

"He's getting harder to catch all the time," said Pauline. "I'm going to ask Daddy if we can tie him in the barn." But when she asked, he refused. He said he didn't have any feed for him, and Buster had to be kept in the lot.

Charlotte heaved a sigh of relief, and she was glad she hadn't taken the halter as she had planned that day. If Pauline had seen it, she would have known Charlotte was riding Buster, and Charlotte wouldn't have been allowed to go into the lot anymore, even if there was plenty of firewood to be had.

Charlotte stayed away from the pasture for a few days. The fear of the snake was still with her, and she still had a clammy feeling on her leg whenever she thought about it. But whenever Buster saw her play with the smaller children in the yard, he ran up to the fence and whinnied. After a few days, she had conquered her fear of snakes and went to the barn and got the halter. She slipped it over his head put her bare toe lightly above his knee and swung up on his back. She found she could ride him at a lope on even ground with her other foot a little ways up in the air. *If I had a belly strap on him like that girl did on her horse, I could probably raise my other leg higher,* she told herself.

Then she slowed him to a walk and grabbed his mane with the halter rope firmly in the other hand. She swung down on his shoulder and hung with just the toe of her other foot up on his back, like she saw the Indians do in pictures in her history book.

Ted came down to the lot, calling to her to hurry up with the wood. He looked around for her. Ma had told him to help her, and he didn't see her until Buster turned around with her clinging to his side. He gasped. He thought she was falling off, but Charlotte swung herself up on the horse's back, then jumped off. She pulled the halter off. "Please don't tell anybody," she begged. "I've been practicing and I can stand on his back, too, but I'm not very good at it."

"I don't believe it," said Ted. "Let me see how you do it."

Charlotte put the halter back on Buster to show him how she did it. "I've fallen off quite a few times," she confessed, "but I can stay on his back all the time now, even if he jumps to one side when he's startled," she added proudly.

Ted was amazed at how she clung to Buster's side when he was trotting. "Show me how," he begged. Charlotte showed him how she did it, but Ted was too small. "You'll have to wait until next fall," Charlotte said. "Then I'll show you. Pauline and Clara will be in high school then, and Ma won't care if we ride him."

It was nearly a week before school started when a farmer who lived south of Harrold told Daddy he could use some help for a few days. There wasn't much gas in the car, and they needed it to go to Harrold to take the cream in to trade for groceries, so Daddy decided to ride Buster.

Buster was in a mischievous mood. When Daddy tried to coax him in with a small pan of oats from a sack he had saved to feed only the work horses, he swung his head and whinnied, then dashed away wildly into the woods with his mane and tail flying.

Daddy called the girls to help corner him, but Charlotte was washing dishes, and Daddy told her to stay in the house until she was finished.

Buster would not be caught. Ma came up from the lot and told Charlotte she guessed Daddy would have to take the car after all.

"I think I can catch him," said Charlotte. "He comes to me all the time when I go after firewood."

Ma took Charlotte by the hand, and they went down to the lot. She called out to Daddy: "Charlotte thinks she can catch him. Let's let her try."

"How do you know he'll come to you?" Daddy asked.

"I've been feeding him sweet clover," Charlotte answered.

"Everybody get out of here, so Buster can't see you," ordered Daddy. "Get some clover, Charlotte, and see if you can coax him in. It's getting late, and I told the men I'd be there early."

Charlotte went to the creek bank on the other side of the fence and picked an armful of clover. Daddy opened the gate, and she went into the pasture. Daddy, with the bridle in his hand, stood off to one side. Buster ran up to Charlotte for his treat and Charlotte twisted her hand in his mane. Buster was nervous but he settled down and ate with Charlotte petting him and soothing him with her voice.

"See if you can get him to come to the fence," prompted Daddy. "I'll hand you the bridle. I'll tell you how to put it on."

"I know how. I help Elaine bridle her horse all the time at school," said Charlotte, and Daddy handed her the bridle. She put it on and led him out of the lot and handed the reins to Daddy. He led him to the barn to saddle up, then mounted and rode him by the house and stopped. "I don't want to hear any more noise about who rides this horse," he announced. "Whoever I say can ride him, gets to ride him. And if Charlotte is going to feed him, she can ride him." Pauline let all the younger children learn to ride him when Daddy was around, but when he was gone, she claimed Buster for her own and wouldn't let anyone else but Clara on him.

When Charlotte was a junior in Canning High School, she stayed on the Clayton Nye farm, where she worked for her room and board. They had a brown saddle horse they called Babe who was part Thoroughbred, part Morgan. Babe was very fast, but dangerous to ride because she had been spoiled by a previous owner and had what was called a hard mouth. She was difficult to pull to a halt and when she became excited, she could not be stopped until she ran out of breath.

The first week Charlotte worked at the Nye farm, she was invited to a get-acquainted party at the school and because she would be coming home after dark, Mr. Nye decided she would ride Babe. "You can tie her in the school barn," he said.

"You'll have to stop at Samco's store and get a paper plate," said Mrs. Nye, whose name was Pearl, as she gave Charlotte a spoon and fork to put in her pocket. "Tell him to put the package on our bill and give you a plate to take to the party."

Mr. and Mrs. Samco owned the merchandise store in Canning. They sold groceries, hardware, and clothing. They also ran the cream station and the post office, which was located in the front end of the store. Charlotte knew the Samcos. Daddy and Ma sometimes sold cream and bought groceries there in the summer.

Charlotte hadn't done much riding in a saddle. The only times she did was when John Gerlt or Jack and Frank

Garrigan let her ride their horses, and the stirrups were always too long. She was used to riding bareback and she was a little nervous when Clayton brought Babe to the house for her to mount. "You'll have to get on so I can adjust the stirrups to your leg length," said Clayton.

"I probably don't need them," answered Charlotte. "I'd better adjust them for you, anyway," said Clayton. "If she sees something she isn't used to, she might spook and you'll have to pull hard on the reins to keep her from bolting. Are you sure you can ride her?" he asked. "I can take time to drive you in the pickup." Nyes had a dairy farm with lots of cows to milk and care for, and Charlotte knew that Clayton did not have time to take her to the party.

"I'm sure I can ride her," Charlotte said. "I'm just used to riding bareback."

"If you can ride bareback, I'm sure you can ride in the saddle," said Clayton, and he stepped aside while Charlotte gathered up the reins and put her feet in the stirrups. She trotted down the road and went through the gate, over the railroad track and past Lake Chesley, marveling at Babe's smooth gait. "You're a very nice horse," she told her as she patted her on the neck. "You and I will get along just fine."

Mr. Samco was sitting on the porch of the store talking to Mr. Fisher, who had a small farm on the edge of Canning. Charlotte told him what she wanted, and she started to dismount Babe to go into the store.

"You don't need to get off," said Mr. Samco. "I'll bring it to you." He went into the store and got a paper plate and handed it to Charlotte. Charlotte reached out to take it and tuck it under her jacket. Babe caught the flash of the white plate from the corner of her eye and became very frightened. She snorted, dropped her head, then leaped up into the air and started off at a high gallop, leaping and sun fishing all the way. Mr. Samco sprang for her bridle, but she was gone.

"Drop the plate!" shouted Mr. Samco, but Charlotte didn't hear him. She shoved the plate inside her jacket against her chest and grabbed the reins with both hands to rein her in, but Babe couldn't be stopped. She stormed up the road and jumped the fence into the churchyard. By that time, Charlotte was pulling on one rein, turning Babe's head so that she had her nose nearly to her chin. Babe finally stopped short, blowing and snorting and trembling all over.

"You poor thing," said Charlotte, as she patted her neck. "You were scared of that plate, weren't you? Just be quiet. I won't let you see it again."

Charlotte talked to her until she calmed down. Mr.

Samco and Mr. Fisher had cut across the back lot and arrived at the gate just as Charlotte was dismounting to open it. They were frightened. They expected to find Charlotte in a heap beside the road.

"Why didn't you drop the plate when I yelled?" asked Mr. Samco. "I suppose it's lost by now. I'll get you another one and take it to the schoolhouse for you."

"You don't have to," answered Charlotte. "I have it under my jacket where she can't see it."

"Where did you learn to ride like that?" exclaimed Mr. Fisher. "I thought you were a goner! I would have sworn nobody could have stayed on her before she leaped that fence!"

Charlotte didn't say anything. She was too shy to talk to anyone she didn't know. For a while, she wasn't sure she could stay on her either, and she was glad for the experience she had in riding Buster and the work horses' colts.

She opened the churchyard gate, led Babe through and then closed it, talking to her all the time. She put her foot above her knee and jumped into the saddle, then rode her back down to the road to the school barn and put her in a stall. She went into the schoolhouse to the party, where she became reacquainted with all her old friends and met her new teachers.

The next day, the news was all over town about Charlotte riding a runaway horse while hanging onto a paper plate, then calmly going to the school party without telling anybody what had happened.

Charlotte loved Babe. When she became editor of the school paper, she rode her through the vicinity, gathering news items. Most of the time Nye's son Eldon, who was nine years old, went along riding on his pony. Charlotte never had any more trouble with Babe running away. Whenever she was startled, Charlotte would soothe her by talking to her and pulling on one rein to turn her head and she would settle down, trotting at her easy gait.

Buster settled down to be a fine saddle horse, and all of the Uecker children learned to ride on him. He lived a long time, and Pauline, Clara, Marie and Charlotte's children all rode him when they visited their grandparents.

The Washing Machine

"It's Clara's turn to stay home from school to help me wash clothes," Ma announced. "I want Pauline and Marie to help her carry the water to put in the wash boiler before they go to school. Daddy chopped the wood before he went to work. Ted and Charlotte are supposed to carry it in and put it in the wood box."

Washing clothes for a big family was a great deal of work, especially since the Ueckers didn't have running water or a washing machine. In the winter, the tubs were put on the bench that was used at the table during meals. The wash boilers, tubs, and baskets and the piles of dirty clothes took up a huge space in the kitchen, and it took nearly all day to get the washing completely done.

Clara and Pauline took several trips to the well, each carrying a big milk pail full of water, while Marie carried a smaller one. They filled the wash boiler that sat on the stove, while Ma filled the firebox with wood. She also mixed up a batch of bread so she could bake it while the oven was hot from heating the wash water.

"I'm glad this is the last of it," said Pauline, as she and Clara took two more trips to the well to carry enough water to fill the big rinse tub with cold water.

Pauline, Marie, Charlotte, Ted and Goldie picked up the dinner pails and books and went off to school, and Clara stayed home to watch George and Florence and help as much as she could with the washing.

When Pauline and Clara left home to go to high school, it was Charlotte and Marie's turn to stay home to help. First, they separated the clothes into three piles: whites, coloreds, and heavy dark clothes such as overalls.

When the water in the boiler became hot, Ma used a big aluminum pan with a handle on it to dip water from the boiler into a tub that she had put on a big wooden box. She added some cold water and lye soap that she had cut up. She also put lye soap in the water that was still in the boiler on top of the stove. She put the dirty white clothes into the tub and added enough cold water so she could put her hands in to scrub them. She then started stomping them with a metal cone shaped apparatus (called a "stomper") that had a smaller cone inside it with holes in it. The stomper had a long handle protruding from the center of the cone. Using the stomper would force water up through the clothes and help get some of the dirt out.

After she and Clara stomped the clothes for a while, Ma put the washboard into the tub. It was a rectangular shaped board about fourteen inches wide and twenty-five inches long. It had a small ledge that held the bar of lye soap that was used for scrubbing clothes. Below the ledge was a sheet of corrugated metal that went to the bottom of the board, except for the last four or five inches where the legs were attached. The legs were submerged below the water in the tub. Ma would place a soiled garment over the metal and pull the bar of soap over it. Then she would scrub it over the corrugated metal to get the dirt out. It was hard work, and she and whoever was helping her at the time would take turns, though she did most of it. After scrubbing them, she would put the white clothes into the rinse water. She added a little bluing to the rinse water from a bottle labeled "Mrs. Stewarts," because she said it would make the clothes get whiter when they dried. After rinsing and wringing out the white clothes and putting them in a basket, she would stomp and scrub the colored clothes, wring them out with her hands and put them in the rinse water.

The rinse water was cold, and after stirring the clothes around, she would pull them up and wring them with her hands and put them in a basket. When the basket was full, whichever child was helping her would take them out and hang them on the clothes line. When the water became dirty, she would pour it out and put the dark heavy clothes and the water from the boiler into the tub. She would add cold water and scrub them on the board.

Wringing the clothes out was the hardest part of the washing, and she had to wring the clothes once after scrubbing them before she put them in the rinse water, and again after taking them out of the rinse water before hanging them. Washing was a tiring process, and it took all day. If the weather was freezing, the clothes still had to be hung outside, then brought in later to finish drying on lines strung across the kitchen. During this time, Ma also kneaded the bread once it rose, put it in the pans, and baked it when it was ready. Even though she had children to help, and when they got older they could help more, it was an exhausting day. Ma was always very tired when washday was over, and her hands were red and rough from scrubbing and wringing clothes.

When baby Charles David, who was called "Sonny," was born in December 1935, Pauline and Clara were in high school. Pauline had a job, so Clara left school for several weeks to help Ma with the baby and do the washing. After she went back to school, Charlotte and

Marie went back to taking turns helping with the washing. They could help scrubbing and hanging clothes, but their hands weren't strong enough to wring them out like Ma did.

One spring day, when Sonny was only a few months old, a traveling salesman who sold spices and kitchenware, sometimes trading them for chickens or old aluminum pans, drove down the rutted hill to the Uecker Place.

The salesman had a washing machine and wringer packed in a box in the back seat of his car, and he told Daddy and Ma he would like to demonstrate it. Daddy went to the well and carried water to put in the boiler to heat, while the salesman unpacked the machine and put the legs on. The tub to the machine had a rounded bottom. It held several gallons of water. There was a movable piece of metal with holes in it on the bottom. It had a bar attached to it on the side that went up above the top of the tub. A piece of wood was inserted in the bar, making a handle. When the handle was pushed back and forth, the metal piece went back and forth up the sides of the tub and the water in the machine was forced up through the holes. A wringer was attached to the other side of the machine. The four legs went out from the tub on a slant, so the machine wouldn't tip over. It had a spigot on the bottom to drain the water out when they were through washing clothes. Ma especially liked that, because it was difficult for her to tip the tubs to pour the water out in pails and then carry them outside to either dump the water or use it to scrub the outdoor toilet. Ma also especially liked the wringer, which was turned with a crank. Wringing out clothes by hand was hard work.

But as much as Ma and Daddy liked the washing machine and wringer, they didn't have the money to buy it. The salesman said he would take some chickens in trade that day, and he would come back two more times for payments amounting to three dollars each. That was a lot of money for the Uecker family, even though they knew the salesman was not making very much profit on the deal. But they always fed the salesman dinner when he came, and he said he appreciated it.

Ma and Daddy decided to buy the washing machine, and they managed to come up with the three-dollar payments when they were due. Washdays were not dreaded nearly as much from then on, and Charlotte and Marie would take turns to help Ma with the washing. They would push the handle back and forth, and the machine did a good job taking the dirt out. Sometimes they had to use the washboard to scrub out heavily soiled clothes, but not very often. They especially liked the wringer because Ma could wring the clothes without getting so tired, and her hands became soft and smooth again. The clothes were easier to hang on the line, and they dried much faster.

Ma used the washing machine for many years, until she and Daddy bought one powered by a gasoline engine after they moved to Giddings. When the Rural Electrification Act brought electricity to the farm in the early 1950s, Ma bought a washing machine with an electric powered wringer. Even though water still had to be carried from the well and heated on the stove, washdays were much easier.

When Charlotte got married in 1945, she lived on a ranch in southeastern Hughes County known as the Big Bend. She cooked and washed clothes for several hired men as well as her husband Chas and family of five. At first, the water was carried and heated and the washing done just as it was when she lived on the creek, but soon they got a washing machine that ran on power from a 32-volt wind charger that charged a few batteries. The batteries generated the electricity that ran the washing machine, though they could only be used to wash clothes when the wind blew. When she and her family moved into their new house in 1948, they put up a bigger wind charger that charged a larger number of batteries that sat on two long benches in the basement. They had water piped to the house from an artesian well and heated the water with a gas water heater. But wash-days were still hard work. The clothes had to be hung on the line, and Charlotte would be very tired when the day was over. When she brought the clean, fresh clothes in from the line to fold them, she would think of how the laundry was done when she was growing up and her washday didn't seem so bad, even though she washed clothes for her family of five little ones, her husband, and two or three hired men who boarded with them.

Beans

Ring, the family dog, died when the Uecker family lived on the side hill. The children missed him very much. They moved to the Lamphere Place not long after, and Daddy was too busy working on the county road south of Harrold to look for another dog.

When the family moved to the Congdon Place down the creek, they still did not have a dog. One morning, Daddy took Ted and Goldie with him to John Gerlt's farm, which was a just a small distance up the creek. John had a beautiful white collie with a tan spot over her eye that reached up to her ear. Her name was Fannie. Fannie was an intelligent dog. When John told her to lie down or sit up, she obeyed immediately. When he told her to fetch the cows to the barn, she went out to the pasture and brought them in. If he had a nervous cow or pig in the barn, he would tell her to go to the haymow, and she would climb to the steps to the mow and peer down over the edge.

On this day, John told Ted and Goldie he had something to show them. He took them to a manger in the barn where Fanny was nursing five small pups. Goldie picked up a black and white pup and ran over to him, crying, "Can I have him?" John was amused because Goldie, who was very shy, had never spoken to him before. He answered. "He has to be with his mother for some time yet, but when he is weaned, I'll let you know and you can come get him."

When Ring was weaned, Goldie and Ted had their dog. The older children named him Ring, because he looked a lot like their beloved dog that died.

Ring was as obedient and smart as his mother, but he caught distemper from another neighbor's dog. One day he disappeared up the creek and never came back. Ma said he went away to die, and the family should be glad he wasn't suffering any more. The children were very sad, though, and Daddy promised he would find them another dog.

When Franklin D. Roosevelt became President in 1933, his administration established programs building roads and dams, improving rural areas and providing work for people who were affected by the drought and the Great Depression. Daddy and many of the neighbors were now able to provide for their families. Daddy was close enough to a work project building a dam south of Harrold that he could drive the team from home to the project before daylight in the morning and could come home every night. Sometimes it was already dark when he got home after a long day of hard work. The team was used in building the dam, and he was paid extra for their effort.

The Roosevelt administration also provided a chance for rural children to go to high school. Pauline and Clara started to high school in Blunt, where they stayed in a dormitory paid for by the government. Ma and Daddy were very proud they would be able to get a high school education.

Every morning, Marie, Charlotte and Ted would put hay and water in the wagon and a bucket of oats. One of them would stand by the water barrel in the wagon, and the other two would fill pails of water and hand them up to be emptied in the barrel. They took turns on who was to empty the buckets. By that time, Ma would have Daddy's lunch prepared and breakfast ready, then she would wake Daddy. They would all eat breakfast together. Daddy would harness the team, hitch them up and go on his way while it was still dark. The children would finish the chores while Ma packed their school lunches, then they would clean up for school, pick up their lunch pails and books, and go on their way to Crocus Hill for the day.

One day, Daddy was driving the team and wagon by a farmer's place on his way home from work when he saw some pups playing with the farmer's children. He stopped, and the farmer told him he would be glad to give him one of the pups when they were weaned. A few weeks later, when Daddy was driving by, the farmer came out of the barn with a big pup in his arms and put him in the wagon. Daddy looked at the awkward creature and asked, "What's his name?"

"We call him Beans," said the neighbor, handing Daddy a piece of rope to tie around his neck so he wouldn't jump out of the wagon. "You'd better keep him tied up for a while," he said. "He might want to come home. He's attached to my kids."

"I'm glad he likes kids," answered Daddy. "I have plenty of my own."

When Daddy got home, he drove up to the house and handed the pup down to Ted. "Here's your dog," he said. "Find Ring's chain and collar and tie him up."

Pauline and Clara had come home from Blunt early on Friday for the weekend. "What an ugly dog," Pauline said. "What's his name?"

"Couldn't you find one like Ring?" asked Ma. "I thought Mr. Gerlt was going to give us one of Fannie's new pups when she had them."

"No." said Daddy. "Fannie was sick, too, and she didn't have pups. It's a wonder she didn't die too, when Ring did. This pup's name is Beans."

"Beans?" echoed Ma and the children.

"You can name him something else," answered Daddy as he started toward the barn to unhitch the team.

"Beans," laughed Ted. "I like his name. I'm going to call him Beans."

Beans grew up to be a big dog. His undercoat was tan with black hairs on top. The children loved him, and he loved them. At first, he was so clumsy, he knocked them down when he was playing with them, but he was never rough. When George started to crawl, Ma would put him on the porch and Beans would get between him and the edge so he wouldn't fall off. If Goldie or Ted wandered too far from the house, he would go after them and bark. Then Ma would go to the door and call them back.

Charlotte loved him, too, and she thought he was beautiful. He went with her when she had to go up the creek to get firewood for the kitchen stove. He went with her when she walked after the milk cows. When she herded turkeys, he was always with her. He followed, her, Marie, Ted and Goldie to school and they would have to send him back. He would come after them if they were late getting home.

The jackrabbits during the thirties were very thick. Daddy and the neighbors didn't like them, as they got into the hay yards and ate their precious feed for the livestock. Daddy trained Beans to keep the rabbits away from the hay. Beans loved to chase them. They would run from him and circle back while he chased them. Then he would turn and run back to catch up to them as they came around the circle. Beans ate lots of rabbits.

Clara and Pauline had transferred to Canning High School from Blunt and when Charlotte and Marie started to high school in Canning as well, the school board closed Crocus Hill School because Ted, Goldie and George were the only remaining students. Canning was too far to go back and forth to school each day, so Ted, Goldie and George moved with Pauline, Clara, Charlotte and Marie into an apartment in Canning. Because their school had closed, the school board paid Ma and Daddy to board the younger children in Canning.

That year, Pauline and Clara were seniors and Charlotte and Marie were freshmen. Ted was in the seventh grade, Goldie the fourth, and George in the second. They lived in the apartment in Canning during the week, and the older girls took care of the younger children when they weren't in school. Every weekend, Daddy and Ma, Florence and baby Sonny came to bring them home. Marie, Charlotte, Ted, Goldie and George would get very homesick. They missed Daddy, Ma and the two little ones, and they missed the farm on Chapelle Creek. They missed Buster, the little saddle horse, Rosie and her colt and Bob and Dick, the workhorses. They missed the milk cows and even the pail-fed calves that often knocked them down to get at their buckets of skim milk. They missed Beans, and he missed them. He would meet the car five miles from home, running alongside and barking all the way. When they left to return to school, he would follow the car until Daddy got out and sent him home.

In 1938, Pauline and Clara graduated from Canning High School. When school started the next fall, Ma moved with all the younger children to Harrold where they went to school. Florence started in the first grade in Harrold, and Charlotte and Marie transferred to Harrold for their second year of high school. Charlotte couldn't wait until she got home on weekends. Even though she spent most of the weekends gathering and chopping wood to take back to Harrold for the cook stove, she didn't mind. With Beans beside her, she pulled in branches, sawed them with her little bucksaw or chopped them to cook stove length, and put them in a big box to take to town. She was home, and she was happy.

During the spring of 1939, Daddy, Pauline and Clara moved the family to a farm a few miles south of their Chapelle Creek farm. The new farm was across the road from Giddings, where there was a rural school for the grade school children. Charlotte and Marie went back to Canning High School, where they worked for their room and board during the school year.

Beans was pleased. He had most of the children home with him again, and he never left their side when they were outdoors. When Charlotte came home, she still went for firewood to the creek, which was some distance away, and he was always by her side.

Charlotte and Marie finished high school in Canning in 1941. Pauline married Delton Starkey in December 1940, and Clara married Jack Garrigan in February of 1941. Marie got married that fall to Sam Hieb and moved to a farm southwest of Harrold. Charlotte went to Wessington Springs Junior College, where she earned her teaching certificate. She was home for a weekend from teaching school when Beans died in 1944, and they buried their faithful friend in a little plot in the backyard.

AN AFTERWORD
by the author

The Uecker family moved to the Ditzler Place in 1922. The Ditzler Place was located on North Chapelle Creek (pronounced "Shapelle Crick" by all who lived in the area) a few miles south of Harrold, South Dakota. When they moved, the family had three daughters. The first two were born when the family lived in Gann Valley. The eldest, named Phyllis Pauline after Ma and her cousin, was born in 1917 and was ten years old. Next was Clara Amelia, born in 1919. She was named after Dr. Clara McManus, who helped when she and Pauline were born, and Ma's mother, Amelia Schenegge. The youngest, Anna Marie, was named after Daddy's sister Anna, and Ma's sister Mildred Marie. She arrived in 1921 after the family moved from Gann Valley to the Manley Place in the Big Bend area near DeGrey. Dr. Martin and Mrs. Henry Big Eagle helped when she was born. When they lived on the Manley Place, Daddy worked training teams of horses for Ma's mother Amelia and her brother Fred.

After Marie was born, the Ueckers moved to the Krull Place on Chapelle Creek where they lived for nearly two years. Ma and Daddy used part of their wages from working on the Manley Place to buy a team of white horses called Rosie and Blossom as well as the team's harnesses and a wagon. They spent the rest of their wages on milk cows, pigs and some farm machinery.

The Krull Place was small and the house was very cold, so Daddy started looking for another farm. He found that Mrs. Ditzler, who was a widow, had a farm a few miles south of Harrold for rent. The farm was much bigger than the one they were on, and there was plenty of water in that branch of Chapelle Creek, with big trees shading the buildings. The house was big enough for their growing family. It had a kitchen, living room and bedroom downstairs and two bedrooms upstairs. Ma and Daddy liked the farm, so they rented it.

Charlotte was born on the Ditzler Place in 1923. Dr. Martin, from Harrold, and Mrs. Richards, who lived a short distance away, came to help when she was born. Charlotte, who had no middle name, was named after her Dad, whose name was Charles. Ma said the hired man, Ervin Clark, named her, as they had only picked out a name for a boy before she was born and couldn't agree what to call her.

Ted, whose full name was Theodore Martin, was born two years later in 1925. And Daddy again went to the Richards farm, a short distance away, to get Mrs. Richards to stay with Ma while he went after the doctor.

Ted was named after Ma's brother, Ted Schenegge, and Dr. Martin.

Ma, who was called "Polly" by all who knew her, was a small woman with golden brown hair and big gray eyes. She liked to whistle and sing. She could ride a horse very well and helped Daddy with all the chores. Sometimes they hired a neighbor girl to watch the children, and she would help Daddy mow hay or pick corn. She was born in Iowa in 1893 and moved to Ree Heights, South Dakota with her family when she was twelve years old. She helped her parents on the farm until she met Daddy.

Daddy was a big, tall man with curly red hair and bright blue eyes. Everybody called him "Charley." He was born in Nebraska and, in 1906 when he was 23, moved to Vivian, South Dakota with his brother Dave and other family members, where he filed for a homestead. He broke teams of horses for a living and did farm work for whoever needed him. He also hired out with his team to work on the railroad being built west from Fort Pierre, and hauled rocks for building the courthouse in Pierre. He met Ma in 1912 when he and his brother, Dave, drove their teams to Hand County to pick corn. They were married in Gann Valley the next year.

Their children all had white hair and dark blue eyes. Ted and Marie's hair was curly like Daddy's. Daddy kept their hair cut short, because it was easier for Ma to manage with so many of them to care for.

Charlotte began first grade at the age of five at Happy Hollow Rural School in Webster Township. Her teacher was M. M. Smith. He was apparently a good reading teacher, as Charlotte and her sister Marie, who also began school while he taught, both could read very well.

The family then moved to the Lamphere Place in Raber Township, and Charlotte went with her sisters to Crocus Hill School. The family moved the next year to the Congdon Place, then owned by Harry Hoy, a little way down the creek where Charlotte lived until she was fifteen. Her teachers at Crocus Hill were Dena Krull, Alma Lindberg, Mary Ellen Byrum (Hansen), and Zetta Loughlin (O'Donnell). Charlotte graduated from the 8th grade on the Hughes Co. Honors Roll in May 1936. She was twelve years old.

Because she was so small and young, Ma and Daddy kept her out of school until the next year, when she and Marie began their freshman year together at Canning High School where Pauline and Clara were seniors. Because Crocus Hill School was closed, Ted, George and Goldie also attended school in Canning and stayed with the older girls in a building called King's Store during the school week. The next year after Pauline and

Clara graduated from high school, Ma moved with Charlotte, Marie, Ted, Goldie, George, Florence and Sonny into an apartment in the Kinyon House in Harrold, and Charlotte and Marie attended Harrold High School their sophomore year. That spring, the family moved to the Hanks Place at Giddings, north of DeGrey, South Dakota, and the younger children were able to attend grade school at nearby Giddings School. Charlotte and Marie went back to Canning High School where Charlotte worked for her room and board on Clayton and Pearl Nye's farm while Marie worked for the school janitor, Austin Low, and his family.

Charlotte's duties consisted of housework, washing and ironing, feeding pigs, watching three little boys and getting up at night and stirring milk that stood cooling in cans, as this farm was on the milk route to Pierre. The work, though hard, was enjoyable as Clayton and Pearl were fine people and did a lot to contribute to a pleasant high school time. They had concern for a young girl who was a middle child and as such, had been given relatively little attention. When Charlotte graduated from high school, Pearl and Clayton bought her a prom dress and accessories. If they hadn't, she wouldn't have been able to go to her senior prom, even though she had made the decorations and had done all of the artwork.

She worked for the Harold Fischer family just outside of Canning during her senior year. He was the section boss for the railroad. She did general housework and took care of their small children. She was quarantined for six weeks during her senior year because she had been exposed to scarlet fever though she never came down with it. She still worked at the Nye farm on weekends and for several weeks after she graduated as she was saving money to go to college.

When she graduated from high school, Charlotte was contacted by a Minneapolis art institute to receive a scholarship. The decision was made from artwork that the Canning School Superintendent Harold Atz had sent to them. However, her parents objected, and since she was only seventeen when she graduated, she was unable to go. She still worked for neighbors in the fields, though, hoping she could raise enough money to go on her own.

The next fall, Ma's sister Millie Abnernathy heard of her dilemma and felt she should have a chance to attend college. Aunt Millie came and got her to work for a time on their farm in Buffalo County. Aunt Millie then took her to Wessington Springs Junior College, where she was able to work part of July and August at the college before she enrolled in a one-year "normal school" program to obtain her teacher's certificate. She graduated and obtained her first grade certificate in the spring of 1942.

World War II had started in December 1941. This made a big difference in the farming community, as so many young men were in the army. During the summer after she graduated from Wessington Springs, Charlotte worked on farms, turning windrows of grain over as it had rained and they were beginning to mold. She also worked for a family south of Blunt to earn enough money to buy clothes so she could teach school. She worked the summer of 1943 at Tim and Doris Scherlie's White Palace Grocery in Pierre. On weekends, she shocked grain for local farmers.

Charlotte's first year of teaching was at Riverview School in southwest Raber Township, a little ways from DeGrey. She rode a saddle horse part-time and walked part-time from the Uecker family home, which was nearly five miles away. During bad weather, she stayed at the schoolhouse, which was fixed up for a teacherage. The next year, she taught at Hilltop School in Webster Township and the next year, at Beth Eden School in Pleasant Valley Township. During that time, she worked in the fields on weekends in the fall, then did secretarial work for Carlos Westover, the Superintendent of Hughes

County Schools. In return, she was allowed to use the mimeograph in the office to run off a newspaper called *The Raber Tumbleweed* (patterned after one by the same name edited by Grace Steiner and George Mathews for boys in WWI). She edited and typed the newspaper with material provided with the assistance of her pupils for the young men from the community who served in the Armed Forces during World War II. The newspaper, which was a project of the Young Citizens League in the Raber, Webster and Pleasant Valley rural schools, became very popular and copies were sent to soldiers beyond the community and outside the state.

Charlotte married Charles Agar Hyde on June 3, 1945 and moved to his ranch in south Raber Township. This is in the area called Big Bend. Charlotte and Chas, as he was called, had five children: Jerilyn, Terrill, Charles, Dan and Ross. Chas had a big sheep operation when they first got married, and Charlotte cooked for sheepherders and shearers. They had four steady men working on the place who made their home with them: Chas's brothers Stewart ("Bub") and Russell Hyde, Don Eberhard, and Don ("Bart") Bartlett. Bub married Charlotte's sister Clara after her first husband, Jack Garrigan, died suddenly in 1948, and Bart married Charlotte's sister Florence. They herded sheep and helped with the haying.

Russell usually spent weekends and slow time with his family in Sully County.

When their oldest child Jerilyn was nearly a year old, on August 27, 1947, just a week before Terri was born, their house burned down while the family was in Pierre. This was a big hardship. An old one-room building that had been used for a schoolhouse in the Big Bend ("Pocket") area was moved to the place and Charlotte and Chas moved into it with the two babies. Charlotte cooked for eight to ten men twice daily until Christmas. She did most of the washing for herself and the babies on the scrub board, and a neighbor did the men's clothes. They started building a new house, but the builder was in a bad car accident in which his wife was killed, and he and their daughter spent months in the hospital. As a result, they weren't able to move into the new house until June 1948. While Chas was occupied with building the new house, Chas's brother Bub, Bart and Charlotte's brother George helped with the haying and feeding cattle.

Charlotte and Chas and their family spent thirty-two happy years on the ranch, where Jerilyn and Terri were soon joined by their brothers Charles, Dan and Ross. They were both actively involved in their five children's school, sports, 4-H and rodeo pursuits. However, there were tragic times: Their beloved son Dan died at the age of seventeen as the result of a car accident; Charlotte's brother Sonny also died in a car accident; and Chas became ill with Parkinson's disease in his 60's.

In 1946, they sold the sheep and went into a cattle and grain operation. Chas served on the Raber Township board for many years. Charlotte belonged to the Helping Hand Club, which her mother had helped start in the 1920s. After she had major surgery, she signed up for a correspondence course in Art and joined the Canvasback Art Club in Pierre. Charlotte and Chas lived on the ranch until Chas's illness with Parkinson's disease forced him to enter a nursing home in Pierre in February 1977. Charlotte moved to an apartment in Pierre to be near him. He passed away December 29, 1977. Charlotte stayed on in Pierre, as they had sold the ranch to their youngest son, Ross, and his wife, Deborah. In 1979, she purchased the home in Pierre where she still resides.

Charlotte worked at the Robinson Museum in Pierre, then for Social Services and Archives at the State Library, and later worked at the Heritage Center. She also did contract artwork for the curator at the Robinson Museum. She served as President of the Canvasback Art Club for many years. The Club operated a gallery at the Pierre Mall and later moved to Dakota Avenue for two years. The gallery closed when the building was sold. Charlotte has had four individual art shows and participated in many others together with her fellow artists. She still paints as a hobby.